PRESENTS

The Secret OBAKE CASEBOOK

Tales from the darkside of the cabinet

Books by Glen Grant

Chicken Skin Series

Obake Files: Ghostly Encounters in Supernatural Hawai'i (1996)

A Chilling Tale of Shave Ice: Mrs. Sugihara Haunts a Village (1997)

Pictorial Publications

Hawai'i, The Big Island: A Journey to a Realm of History, Beauty and Fire (1988)

Above the Skies of Paradise: O'ahu (1992)

Above the Skies of Paradise: Hawai'i, The Big Island (1992)

Historical Introductions

Myths and Legends of Hawai'i by King Kalakaua (1990)

Hawai'i's Story by Hawai'i's Queen by Lili'uokalani (1990)

Rape in Paradise by Theon Wright (1990)

Around the World with a King by R.C. Armstrong (1995)

Ancient History of the Hawaiian People by Abraham Fornander (1996)

Co-Authored with Dennis M. Ogawa

Ellison S. Onizuka: A Remembrance (1986)

To a Land Called Tengoku (1985)

Other Publications

Obake: Ghost Stories in Hawai'i (1994)

Honolulu Mysteries: Case Studies in the Life of a Honolulu Detective (1995)

Waikiki Yesteryears (1996)

The Secret OBAKE CASEBOOK

Tales from the darkside of the cabinet

BY GLEN GRANT

with illustrations by Ross Yamanaka

First Printing, October 1997
1 2 3 4 5 6 7 8 9

ISBN 1-56647-183-4

Design
Michael Horton
Illustrations
Ross Yamanaka

All inquiries should be addressed to:
Chicken Skin/Honolulu Time Walks
2634 S. King Street. #3
Honolulu, HI 96826
Email: chickenskin@compuserve.com

Mutual Publishing
1215 Center Street, Suite 210
Honolulu, HI 96816
ph: (808) 732-1709
fax: (808) 734-4094
email mutual@lava.net

Printed in Australia

Like one, that on a lonesome road
Doth walk in fear and dread,
And having once turned round walks on,
And turns no more his head,
Because he knows, a frightful fiend
Doth close behind him tread.

The Rime of the Ancient Mariner
Samuel Taylor Coleridge

A Parental Warning

The Stories in ***The Secret Obake Casebook*** have been compiled from the dark side of the supernatural cabinet file where demonic, sinister and sometimes pornographic forces dwell. In retelling these stories, I have been cautious not to use language or graphic descriptions unsuitable for the young adults who often read my work. However, these tales are not intended for children. The subject matter is honest and forthright without being vulgar, but delves into areas which may be inappropriate for young people.

Table of Contents

Mahalo

The Secret Obake Casebook is based upon hundreds of stories that I have received in the last 26 years from the people of Hawai'i, representing all backgrounds, cultures, ethnicity and stations of life, who have shared one thing in common—they have made contact with the marvelous world of Island spirits. It is impossible to thank these various individuals enough for sharing their experiences with me so that I could assume the responsibility of retelling their stories with new situations, settings and relationships. This has been done to protect your anonymity, while passing along to others the truth of the dark forces that in your life you have encountered and survived. I trust that, if you do recognize yourself in this work, you will be satisfied that your tale was told with respect. If you cannot identify yourself, then I have done my job well.

To give context to these tales, I have consulted several "sources" which I consider the standard works reflecting supernatural traditions in Hawai'i and around the world. Among those cited sources are: Samuel M. Kamakau, *Ka Po'e Kahiko: The People of Old,* translated from the Newspaper *Ke Au 'Oko'a* by Mary Kawena Pukui. (Honolulu: Bishop Museum Press, 1964); Davida Malo *Ka Mo'olelo Hawai'i, Hawaiian Traditions,* translated by Malcolm Naea Chun, (Honolulu: First People's Productions, 1996); Mary Kawena Pukui, E.W. Haertig, & Catherine A. Lee, *Nana I ke Kumu (Look to the Source)*, Vol. I & II. (Honolulu: Hui Hanai, 1972); E.P. Sterling and C.C. Summers, *Sites of O'ahu,* (Honolulu: Bishop Museum, 1978); J. S. Emerson, "Selected from a Kahuna's Book of Prayers," *Hawaiian Historical Society,* (Annual Report, 1917); Dennis Kawaharada, Ancient O'ahu: Stories from Fornander & Thrum, (Honolulu: Kalamaku Press, 1996); Rosemary Ellen Guiley, *The Encyclopedia of Ghosts and Spirits,* (N.Y.: Facts on File, 1992); John Glaister and Edgar Rentoul, *Medical Jurisprudence and Toxicology,* (London: E. & M.S. Livingstone, 1966); Paul Barber, *Vampires, Burial, and Death: Folklore and Reality,* (N.Y.: Yale University Press, 1988); and Traugott K. Oesterreich, *Possession and Exorcism Among Primitive Races, in Antiquity, The Middle Ages, and Modern Times,* (N.Y.: Causeway Books, 1974).

Special thanks is also extended to T. Michele Clark, Museum Specialist, National Park Service, Longfellow National Historic Site, for permission to publish Longfellow's "A Spiritual Letter."

The team of individuals who assisted with this project once again draws upon the professional talents and good friendships of people dedicated to capturing the spirit of Hawai'i's ghost stories with creativity, imagination, respect and "Chicken Skin." These individuals include Jill Staas, who is always there to give support whatever the problem; Arnold Hiura, who is always there to warn me against hackneyed writing; Audrey Muromoto, who protects me from spiritual unpleasantries through daily maintenance of the Hawaiian salt and ti plants in the office; Ross Yamanaka, who captures the dark side of his artistry through haunting illustrations; Michael Horton, who turns stale text into graphic excellence; Bennett Hymer who tolerates my lack of understanding for the meaning of "deadline;" and Betsy Kubota who checks the manuscript for errors of grammar or other inconsistencies. *Mahalo* to you all for your friendship, moral support, and creative energies that have made all our projects progressively reach higher levels of excellence, with a powerful sense of respect and reverence for those things unseen, but felt.

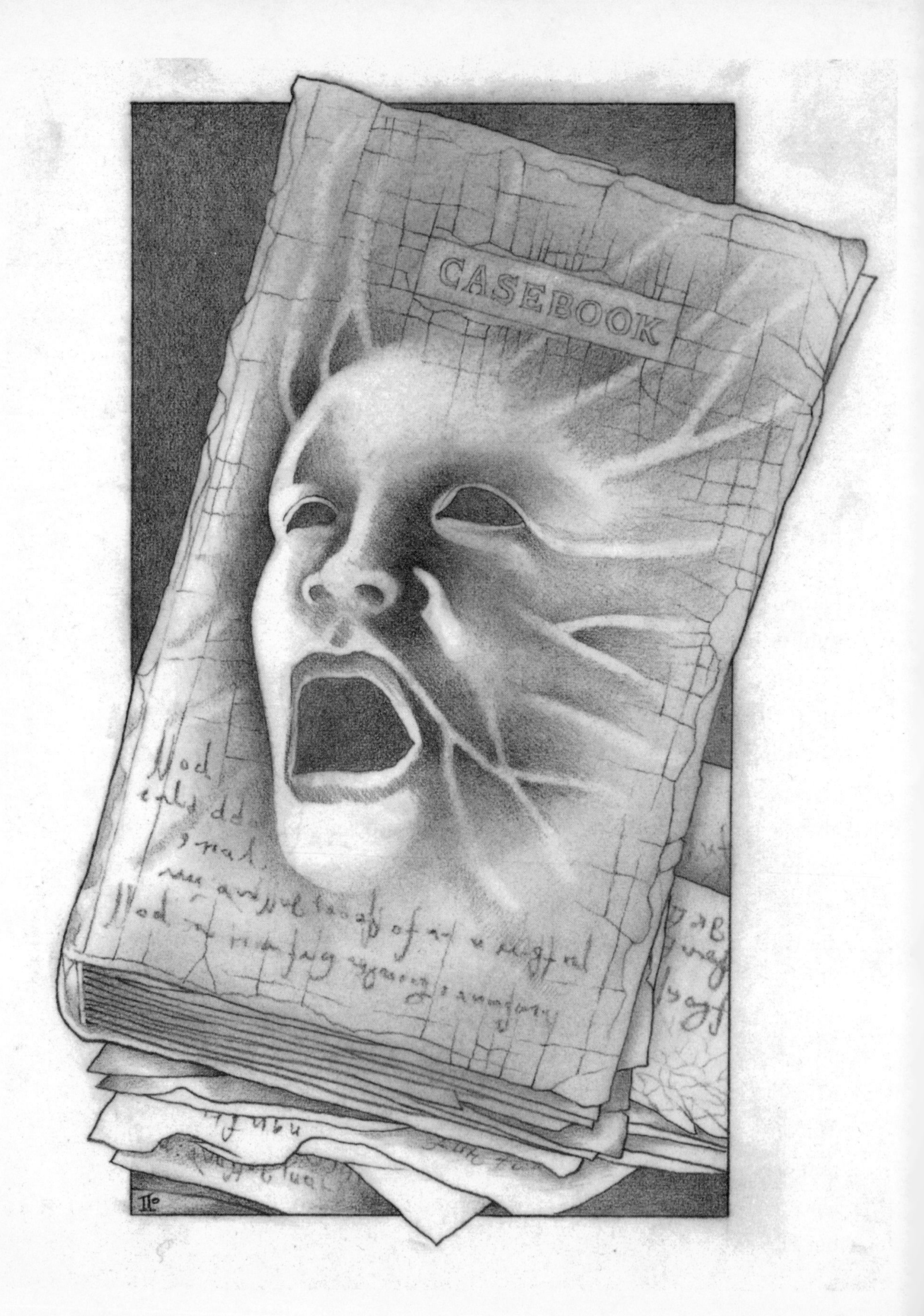
CASEBOOK

The Dark Files Unlocked:

When Frightful Fiends Tread Behind

"*What are* your intentions?"

The question came from a kind, but very concerned, Hawaiian woman who was the deaconess of a Native Hawaiian church located in Kalihi. The religious tenets of the church combined elements of Christianity with Hawaiian spirituality, including the ritual of *wahi i ka Paipala,* or opening the Bible and selecting a passage at random as a means to seek help in a problem. A friend who was a member of the church and knew my interest in supernatural powers intervening in daily life, invited me to one of the services. Later she introduced me to the deaconess as someone who had a lifelong interest in ghost stories. When the deaconess learned that I was telling a ghost storyteller, she asked me point-blank what my intentions were in conducting this type of work.

I had been in Hawai'i only about one year at the time and I was a bit confused at the question. I had never thought about what my intentions were of anything I had thus far done in my life, having recently graduated from the University of California at Los Angeles and having made the first, biggest and only move thus far in my life to the Hawaiian Islands. I tried to explain to the Hawaiian woman that I had a love for collecting, telling and writing down firsthand, allegedly true ghost stories since I was a child. I had inherited my love for supernatural tales from my ghost storytelling father, as well as through my addiction to *The Twilight Zone* television show. I had read every book available on the subject of the paranormal, ghosts and poltergeists and one day I wanted to write my own book on Hawai'i's tales.

"You don't understand, son," she repeated. "What are your intentions in collecting ghost stories?"

Again, I was incoherent in my answer, wandering around the subject without giving a direct answer. Finally, I bluntly admitted that I didn't know why I had wanted to do this. It just seemed like something important to my life and maybe one day to others.

"Was it wrong?" I asked naively.

"Not necessarily," she answered cryptically. "You are very young now and don't know what you are getting into. Just be certain that whatever you do with these things of the spirit, you always do with good intentions. If you don't, then the ghosts you have gathered about you by collecting and telling these stories will become angry and dangerous. They could harm you if your intentions are not *pono.*"

"What are good intentions?" I asked, hoping to be given a guideline to follow.

The deaconess looked wisely at me with a thin smile and said something which probably was the best answer possible. At that time in my life, however, I thought it was the worst possible answer that I could have received.

"You will have to determine what is a good intention for yourself. No one can tell you. You'll have to look into your heart for the answer."

That conversation 25 years ago has, more than any single other piece of advice, shaped the way that I have "dabbled" in Hawai'i's supernatural traditions. The deaconess made me aware of the fact that every time I tell a story, the spirit that is mentioned in the tale listens to determine if I am faithful to the story, if I am respectful of its reality and whether my intentions are "*pono.*" This has been confirmed by the many psychics and other persons sensitive to spirit presence who claim that during my storytelling sessions they have seen many ghosts standing about me, listening with interest to my tales. I am not gifted to see spirits, but on too many occasions I have definitely felt forces about me as if I had invoked them with the story.

This became painfully obvious last year when I was sharing ghost stories with a group of youngsters at Palama Settlement in Kalihi. After the session a small boy tugged at my shirt.

"Sir, when these children leave, may I see you alone?"

Since he must have been only eight or nine years old and the "children" he referred to were young teenagers, his tone seemed oddly adult-like. When we were alone, he explained that he and his mother were gifted to see spirits.

"And I wanted you to know that during your storytelling an elderly

Hawaiian woman with white hair was standing behind you . . .watching you."

A sweep of cold air went over my flesh as I knew once again that my efforts to share the supernatural tales of Hawai'i were being observed by a spirit world. I was especially concerned about the demeanor of the old woman who was watching me.

"Was she smiling or frowning?" I asked the child, anxiously.

"She was smiling. She liked the stories. I just wanted you to know that."

With that said, the young boy walked off, leaving me nervously looking over my shoulder at the unseen spirit that had attended my lecture. I hoped that she saw that my "intentions" were indeed good.

What are my intentions of collecting, preserving and telling the ghost stories of Hawai'i? My purpose is not as a psychic or spiritual healer or someone who wants to be recognized as a "spirit seer." Neither do I seek to be known as an "expert" on the spiritual meaning of material which touches the wonders and mysteries of Hawai'i's deep current of multicultural supernatural traditions. I stand at the edge of that vast unknown realm, with the limitation of flesh shared probably by most of the public. I am no one special or "gifted" to bring from supernatural experiences a convincing theory or philosophy on why such things occur.

Instead, the intention of my storytelling has been to contribute in a tiny way to an island-wide resurgence of cultural pride not only in the diverse traditions of dance, music, art, history and literature, but an awakening awe and respect for things unseen. If collecting, telling and writing about ghosts of Hawai'i has promoted a stronger sense of acceptance of supernatural realities, instilling in the young generation a reverence for the beliefs of their ancestors, then the tales have indeed served a "good intention." If, through my haunted tales, people have a greater love for the past and thereby reach out to touch the lives of the dead generations that still inhabit these Islands, then these tales have done a small service to an Island community facing more urbanization and loss in the twenty-first century.

It is important, then, for the spiritual protection of a ghost storyteller to have certain uncompromising standards to safely and correctly pursue his profession:

Golden Rule Number One:
Never ask someone to tell you a ghost story.

Ghost stories are private, spiritual encounters that must be volunteered, not sought after for the purposes of expanding a repertoire or selling more books. I never ask security guards if their buildings are haunted unless they first volunteer the information. Police officers, nurses, mortuary workers, gravediggers and others who deal with the drama of life and death on a daily basis are never aggressively approached by me in the hunt for a ghost story. I don't intrude upon the private spiritual beliefs of others unless they willingly come forward for their own reasons to share their personal experiences of a ghostly encounter. Stories that are chased after for my own personal gain may bring to me forces that I don't wish to face. However, if the story comes naturally to me from someone seeking advice or merely wishing to share their story through me with a wider audience, then those tales seem filled with truth.

Golden Rule Number Two: Have a commitment to the truth of supernatural realities.

The ghost story requires the storyteller to respect the spiritual truth of the tale. The contribution the story collector makes to the process of storytelling is to emotionally, intellectually and spiritually become one with the material which every day accumulates in his files. In other words, to tell the story effectively, there must be a commitment to the reality of the spirits whose existence is being retold. This doesn't necessarily mean that every story I hear is absolutely, 100 percent true in exactly the way it was collected—or that the interpretation of why the event took place is always invariably supernatural. But the essential truth of the uncanny tales being shared, a faith that ancient spirits can manifest themselves in the modern world, that the spirits of our dead loved ones do indeed walk, must be accepted if good intentions will flow from a lifetime spent walking with ghosts. The storyteller must therefore have the courage to stand up for the material that he collects against the charges of "superstition," "ignorance," or "deception," while making sure that crass exploitation of the sensational is never allowed to go unchallenged.

Golden Rule Number Three: The storyteller must become the story.

A ghost story collector has a responsibility to elevate the tale that he has received—to use creative and intellectual insights to place the tale into the context of a greater meaning so that the audience will be in some fashion enlightened by the fear, humor, wonderment, or other tingling emotions that are felt when one listens to ghostly tales. Hawaiians sometimes call this feeling which creates disturbing skin sensations *'ili 'ouli*—literally, "skin signs."

There are many such feelings types of skin sensations, including feelings of love, fear, awe or anticipation. One special type of skin sign which signals the presence of supernatural beings is when the body is covered in goose flesh, a sensation called *'okakala.* When the storyteller has done his job well, with a love for the spirits which he invokes, then the audience will be overwhelmed by *'okakala.*

"Chicken skin" has become an island-wide term used increasingly to refer to this *'okakala* sensation, as a result of the Chicken Skin conferences, television shows, tours, book series, audio tapes, and weekly *Chicken Skin: The Radio Show* on KCCN 1420 AM which have all step-by-step attempted to collect, retell and elevate the supernatural traditions of Hawai'i for residents and an increasing number of interested persons around the world. Despite this fascinating growth in the popularity of Hawai'i ghost stories, the fundamental question remains the same. "What are your intentions?" Striving to do what is intuitively "right" is both a guiding principle as well as admonition for anyone who takes up ghost storytelling as an avocation or vocation.

The Secret Obake Casebook: Tales from the Dark Side of the Cabinet was thus a very difficult and sometimes nerve-racking book to write. What were my intentions in putting into one volume the stories of murdered spirits, misused Ouija boards, praying to death sorcerers and demonic possession? What spirits were being evoked by retelling these stories? Was I inviting evil forces into my storytelling that would make me and my audience susceptible to their influences? What impact would the stories have on readers of all ages who may be affected by stories that touch upon the unredeemed and the sinister? Once the words are committed to the printed page, then they are ripe for misinterpretation.

For over 10 years I have puzzled over the proper way to share ghost stories in print with an island-wide audience. At first I was concerned whether or not it was even proper for a *haole* from California to put these tales down on paper. When *Obake: Ghost Stories in Hawai'i* received widespread support from various ethnic communities, I felt more secure to share the work that I had originally planned in 1971—*Obake Files: Ghostly Encounters in Supernatural Hawai'i,* which was a compendium of ghost stories, introducing a wide range of supernatural motifs, ghostly types and haunted places in a manner that was intended for both entertainment as well as reference.

During the compilation and writing of *Obake Files,* it became apparent that certain stories didn't belong in the book—not because they weren't part of the original files or were somehow untrue, but because essentially they were too negative. As I was trying to balance being informative with satisfying the reader's need to feel the tingling of the skin called *'okakala,* some stories just seemed too sinister to be placed next to more spiritually uplifting material such as visions of Pele, nightmarchers, fireballs, *Menehune,* family spirits, or voices of our loved ones coming back from the grave. While choking ghosts, calling spirits and supernatural beasts were included in *Obake Files,* there was always a bit of whimsy mixed with fear in the retelling of the tales of the faceless woman or cannibal dogs. These supernatural entities could be benign as well as frightening; their existence could be dismissed as merely "urban legend."

But what was I to do with a category of story which was as much a part of Hawai'i as the guardian spirits, but in its character was essentially demonic, evil, murderous or insipidly vicious? If it is true that in the retelling of a story you bring the spirits to you, then I certainly didn't want these types of demons visiting my home or office; I didn't want anyone picking up such a book to be assaulted by such beings.

Yet, to neglect the darker side of Hawai'i's supernatural traditions is perhaps to paint too roseate a picture for those who may be tempted to go beyond just listening to a story and to actually think about seriously making contact with spirits of the other world. How could I simply dump all these files into a locked, hidden casebook and then deny that malevolent forces also have a presence in the mysterious realm of Hawai'i's supernatural traditions?

The Secret Obake Casebook is therefore an effort to reveal the dark side of the ghostly cabinet, to share the stories I have been reluctant to tell or conjure up through the written word. For the safety of myself, my staff and the reader, I have therefore followed certain procedures in the creation of this work.

1. Before the project began, our offices, my desk, files and secret casebook were blessed by the Koboji Temple for the purposes of exorcising any spirits which may attach themselves to us for malevolent reasons. During the blessing, a strong presence moved through our Mo'ili'ili offices, brushing several people. Hawaiian salt and *ti* leaves were positioned in the office during the entire project at the direction of a priest with the Koboji Temple so as to ensure the continued safety of all persons.

2. All stories were liberally fictionalized in terms of people, situations and places so that the entities attached to the haunting would not be strongly invoked. No name, place name or specific incident contained in these stories ever took place. . .*maybe.* Only I know what specifically is true or untrue in the stories. Do not, therefore, attempt to draw any conclusions about a

building, person or site from these ghostly encounters. You will be almost certainly wrong.

3. The fact that children and young adults frequently read my work with or without the permission of their parents has necessitated a tempering of the tales as concerns vulgarity, obscenity or overt sexuality. Consequently, I have censored the stories as much as possible so that young minds will not be polluted by what essentially were sometimes the most debasing aspects of human existence. However, I can take no further responsibility for the consequences that *The Secret Obake Casebook* may have on impressionable minds. In an age of media violence and open sexuality, the stories may seem in fact rather tame for some youth. Yet, the fact that these tales stem from deeper truths about the dark side of supernatural entities can become more unsettling in time than any silly horror film. Parents are therefore cautioned. Hopefully a message will emerge from these stories for young people—respect things unseen. Don't waste your youthful innocence experimenting with things better left to those with experience and inner psychological strength. There is time enough for you to learn about the dark side of life as an adult.

4. The core truth of the supernatural encounter in each tale must be genuine. No poltergeist, ghost, possession or act of bizarre behavior contained in this work of fiction is fictional. They are all based on what either someone else or I have experienced in real life. The only fictionalization in this book is the nature of everyday reality—the powers of the otherworld are true to what took place. Why these things happened, what scientific rationalization could be applied to understand this phenomenon, I leave to the reader. Take whatever religious, scientific or occult precautions you believe are necessary before or after reading the case files. If these occurrences disturb you, you can keep telling yourself over and over as you read these pages: "This is a work of fiction; this is a work of fiction; this is a work of fiction."

As we open now the secret casebook to share stories left in the past untold, we recognize with humility our own vulnerability and fear of the very things we explore. We gaze upon the artifacts gathered from our journeys into the supernatural—a badge, a spiritual letter, an old photograph and a turtle amulet—as we ponder what unknown forces we are about to unleash. The goal of this book is to make the reader aware that within the cabinet are truly tales of horror. Beyond the veil are beings both radiant and demonic. Have you the courage to peer into the darkness revealed before us? For behind us, on that dark, lonesome road, a frightful fiend doth indeed tread. Dare you even now look back?

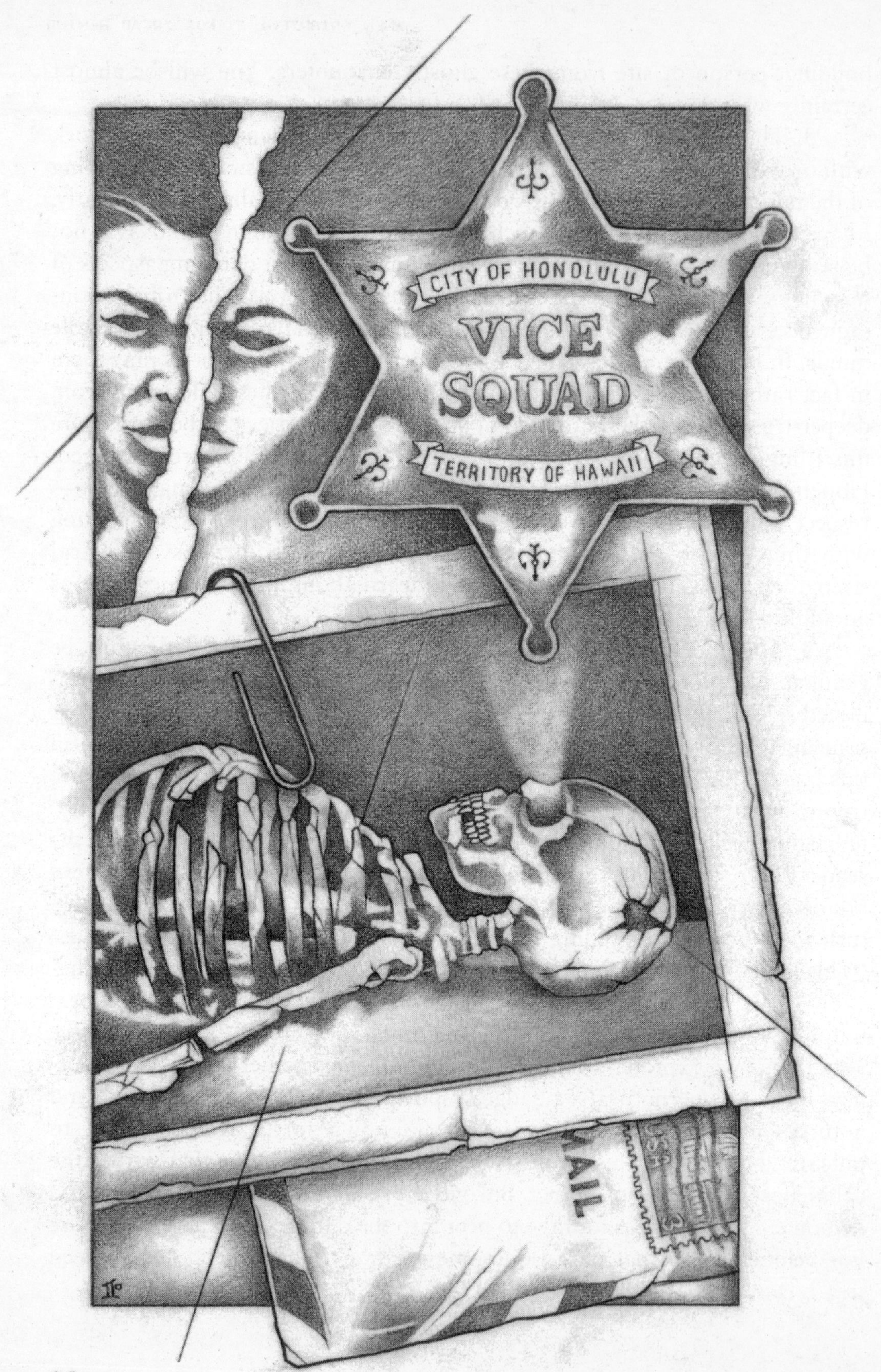
CITY OF HONOLULU
VICE SQUAD
TERRITORY OF HAWAII
MAIL

Dark File 1:

When Evil Breathes and Blood Flows

The small white box in my hands looked like the type of slim carton that is often used by jewelry stores to gift-wrap a precious pendant or gold chain. Examining the object more closely, it was obvious that someone had recycled this container several times, for possibly many purposes. There were dark stains or smudges all over the lid, soiling the once pristine whiteness of a box that had many years before contained a gift of love. The container had aged a little, like a human being, turning slightly yellow with time at the edges.

It had been left on my Mo'ili'ili desk with an envelope dressed simply to "Dr. Grant." One of the staff in our office said that a very pleasant, middle-aged *haole* woman had left it for me that morning. A short handwritten note inside the envelope said very little:

"Glen. I went on your crime tour last Thursday night. It was very enjoyable. Thank you! I thought you might find this interesting so I'd like to give it to you. My husband found it in our backyard a few months ago. If you want to hear the full story, please call me." There was a name and a telephone number with a prefix for the north district of O'ahu.

Using a letter opener, I cut the cellophane tape which sealed the lid of the box and lifted it to see what strange thing someone had decided to send me from the earth in their yard. My reputation as a collector of ghostly tales and mysteries sometimes attracts the oddest assortment of uncanny photographs, peculiarly-shaped rocks, or other "unique" objets d'art. Opening packages at my office is always an adventure into the unknown. Yet, I was honestly not at all prepared for the contents of that worn, old jewelry box.

An old, brass "Vice Squad" badge issued by the "City of Honolulu, Territory of Hawaii" was resting on a wad of white cotton. I had seen this type of historic badge before—in fact, I owned one that was in much better shape than the one in the box. Feeling a bit disappointed that the "treasure" inside the carton was nothing more than a duplicate of something I already owned, I picked it up and turned it over. The pin used to attach the badge to clothing was broken off. The natural curve to the badge was flattened out and the golden brass was discolored with a greenish tint. This "Vice Squad" badge was in a horrible, unusable condition. Why had the woman sent it to me? I thought, as I made a mental note to give her a call later that week.

By 8 Friday evening I was catching up with my correspondence when I finally telephoned the woman who had left me the old badge. She was quite pleasant on the phone, thanking me again for the crime tour, which she thoroughly enjoyed. In fact, she added, she was going to be joining me on my "Ghosts of Old Honolulu" walking tour that following Wednesday. Finally, I thanked her for the badge, saying that I would add it to other memorabilia I had collected from the history of old Honolulu.

"There's a story behind the badge, Dr. Grant," she then said, lowering her voice. "Would you like to hear it? Better yet, would you like to see it?"

See a story? The invitation was intriguing, so I took down her address and made arrangements to meet her and her husband the next day at their Waialua home located in a 10 year old subdivision not far from the sugar mill. The Waialua Sugar Company was at that time still producing the last few crops of the sweet stuff that in the old days had once been gold to the owners. Now, as the gold turned to lead, more and more of the old cultivated fields were being transformed into housing projects to supply the growing population of O'ahu.

Debra Gallegos greeted me enthusiastically at the front door of a modest, single-story Island home set back about 200 yards from the ocean in an area once covered with sugar cane. I remembered her immediately from the crime tour, since she was an unusually tall, haole woman with stunning, long, straight blonde hair. It didn't take much of an imagination to guess that she had moved to the North Shore many years before as a young California "hippie" in pursuit of a surfing paradise. Her husband, John, was a genial, broad-shouldered, part-Hawaiian gentleman in his late forties whose handshake was like a vise. They co-owned a gift shop in Hale'iwa that specialized in beachwear and surfing paraphernalia.

After the usual greetings and introductions, they escorted me into the backyard to "show" me the story of the badge that Debra had dropped off at my office. In the corner of the yard, under a bedroom window, was a three-foot, shallow hole dug evidently by some animal. In a few moments, one of those giant, black-haired dogs with the long snouts and German-sounding names which are famous for eating neighborhood children bounded across the lawn, stopping just before me with a snarl. The beast shoved its nose into my crotch with a menacing sniff as if it were sizing me up for a kill.

"Down, Ikaika!" shouted John. "Down!" Ikaika had put his two massive front paws up on my chest and looked me threateningly in the eye. John pulled him off me by the dog's thick leather collar and, with a swat of the hand on the animal's *'okole,* sent it off to another corner of the yard, where it turned its aggression on a rag doll, which was quickly turned to dust.

"Ikaika first dug up this hole," Debra explained, "about six months ago. One day he just started digging up on this spot."

"And that is where you found the badge?" Somehow the strange tale that I had anticipated was failing to materialize. One day their dog digs up a badge. So what?

"Not exactly, Glen," Debra continued. "Ikaika dug up this. We found the badge later."

Debra handed me a photograph of what the animal had found under the Gallegoses' bedroom window—a skeletal figure clothed in the remains of a decayed, mud-clad suit that clung to the bones like a filthy shroud. The body was laying in a crude grave without the benefit of a vault or coffin. While most of the flesh had rotted away, leaving the bones somewhat picked clean, portions of hair and blackened epidermis still clung to the head. I held the gruesome photograph in my hand as I felt my knees wobble. A collector of ghost stories is not necessarily someone who has the stomach to look at a 50-year-old corpse.

"We called the police immediately," John said, "but to this day they don't know the identity of the corpse. They only know it is a male in his mid-thirties. Based upon the deterioration of the body, they guess he was murdered sometime in the 1920s."

John went on to explain that the victim had been shot in the back of the head with a powerful handgun, probably a Colt .45. An autopsy revealed that the body had been brutally beaten with a massive object that smashed the legs, arms and chest cavity. Whoever the victim had been, he had evidently been tortured before finally having his brains blown out.

"So you found the badge with the body," I pressed, trying to make the connection between the corpse and the "Vice Squad" badge that I turned in my palm. "The victim was a cop?"

"We can't say for sure," Debra answered. "The badge wasn't found with the body. About two weeks after the police took the corpse away, Ikaika dug up a new hole way over there."

Debra pointed beyond the backyard to a section of sugar cane that was growing wild on the border of their property. We walked around a drooping wire fence that was originally used to unsuccessfully cage Ikaika in the yard, and waded through a thicket of cane to another place where the earth had been dug up by the animal. This hole was far more shallow, only about a foot deep and wide.

"One morning Ikaika was barking wildly out here. We at first thought he had trapped a mongoose or rat. But he had uncovered the badge and was snarling at it as if it were an intruder."

The Gallegoses again called the police, who carefully examined the broken, flattened old badge for a few days, with no significant results. It was, the police confirmed, some relic from the old Honolulu Sheriff's office. And it was certainly a strange coincidence that a law enforcement badge would have turned up about 30 yards away from an unidentified murder victim. However, there was no clear connection between the body and the badge. As far as the records of the Honolulu Police Department could reveal, there was no missing "Vice Squad" officer since the department was established in 1932. Any police records before that time were either long ago destroyed or stored in some lost, dusty archive. The dental records matched no one on their missing persons list. Finally, the badge was returned by the police to Debra and John Gallegos as nothing more than an interesting souvenir.

"I really wanted to keep the badge," Debra then volunteered. "John was angry at me, saying that it shouldn't be brought into the house. But something at first told me to keep it. It was like an unsolved mystery."

John gave his wife a slightly annoyed look.

Suddenly, a dark squall passing over Waialua let loose a downfall of heavy, warm droplets of rain as the three of us rushed back to a covered lanai for shelter. The rain pelted the corrugated plastic roof like a thousand tiny gun pellets popping over our heads. Ikaika barked loudly at the squall and then pranced around me, sniffing menacingly at my crotch again. I smiled weakly, patted the beast on his head and muttered something about "good boy."

"So, did the police ask you to keep the holes dug up like that?" I matter-of-factly asked, concentrating more on the protection of my personal parts than on the answer.

"That's the odd thing, Dr. Grant. That's why I called you. We did fill in the holes. We fill them in all the time. It's Ikaika that keeps digging them up!"

Every night the dog goes into the backyard and digs a hole under the bedroom window exactly where the corpse was found. The depth of the hole is always about three feet. Then it runs around the fence and digs a hole at the precise place where the badge was found. When it finishes its hole digging, the animal howls at the darkness as if it can see something invisible to the human eye.

"What do you think?" Debra asked enthusiastically. "Do you think Ikaika can see the spirit of the murdered man?"

"Are there any other manifestations taking place around the yard or even inside your house?"

Debra was just about to answer when John suddenly cut her off.

"No!" he emphatically declared. "Nothing but the dog's funny behavior. My grandmother who's Hawaiian, said that it's a bad omen."

"A bad omen? How do you mean?"

"I don't know," John answered curtly. "Something about a dog digging holes in the yard. That's all. I just want the damn dog to stop acting crazy."

I now noticed that the Gallegoses had placed ti plants under their bedroom window just near the place where the body had been found. Evidently they had taken every precaution they knew, but still Ikaika performed his nightly ritual of digging up the place of the dead. John seemed disappointed that I was neither an exorcist or a parapsychologist who could release the unseen force that had possessed their animal. Of course, I reminded them, there could be a lingering scent that the dog was strangely attracted to, causing it to dig up these two places. There was always a rational explanation for every supernatural tale, I reassured them, if we sought the rational over the preternatural.

Just before I drove back into town, I remembered that I still had the old badge that Debra had left at my office. Now that I had "seen the story," she would probably want her mysterious memento back. I reached into my pocket, retrieved the ghastly object and held it out to the couple.

"I forgot to let you have this back."

"You can have it!" John suddenly said. "We don't need it. You can save it to write about in one of your mystery books."

"Thanks!" I said sincerely, shaking John's hand. "I appreciate it!" As a collector of old memorabilia and a devotee of tales of the bizarre, having that old badge hanging up in my office seemed more than "cool."

Out of curiosity, a few days later I thumbed through one of the important source books that I have always relied upon for interesting contemporary customs and spiritual beliefs concerning the Native Hawaiian community. I had never heard any supernatural lore concerning ill-omens attached to a dog digging holes in the yard of a home. If such a belief existed, I recognized, it may have been recorded in *Nana I Ke Kumu (Look to the Source)* by the Queen Lili'uokalani Children's Center. I checked the index for "dog" in Volume I and found an interesting reference on page 55:

"The dog digs a hole near the house. Any *lua* (pit) is a *ho'ailona* [omen or portent] of death. Fill the hole immediately!

"The dog howls. To this almost universal death portent, the Hawaiian belief adds an explanation. The dog howls because he sees the spirit of the dead or dying person."

Ikaika had certainly been digging a hole near the side of the house—right at the spot where the murdered victim had been found. And the howling of the dog in the night was an omen or portent that the animal was seeing a spirit. Had the ghost of the dead man returned to the place of his burial, first to signal the animal so as to recover his mortal remains, and then simply as an unhappy, restless entity to haunt the place where he had been tragically murdered?

If the restless ghosts are the most feared supernatural entities because they are the most unpredictable, then aren't the victims of murder the most tormented of these phantoms to inhabit the unseen realm that coexists parallel with our physical plane? And does not their torment, transformed by a horrible death into rage, revenge, dread or terror, become a powerful emotional tunnel through which they can escape their eternally doomed existence and, for a brief moment, invade our otherwise mundane realm?

Even the demon-filled world of the early American Puritan settlers of New England was willing to accept the victim of a murder as a true and genuine spirit of the dead. In the seventeenth century, the Puritans denied all ghostly manifestations even of loved ones as lying demons attempting to seduce human souls away from God to the Prince of Darkness. However, when the spirit of a murdered London gentleman appeared before his brother in Boston to correctly inform him of the person responsible for his gruesome death and which boat he was using to escape to New England, even the witch hunter Cotton Mather in his *The Wonders of the Invisible World* declared that this ghost must have been authorized by Divine Providence to seek out final justice. The murdered dead can indeed walk the earth again, he concluded.

These thoughts of murdered souls are unsettling to those of us who are repulsed by the idea of violence or human abuse. The blood and mayhem which has become so fashionable in popular culture and film repels decent, ordinary folk who would not dare to look upon a mangled corpse or be tempted to contemplate the gory product of a serial killer. But *The Secret Obake Casebook* is unfortunately filled with these most sinister episodes in the history of the human heart which has left upon the evil spirit of murderers the indelible mark of Cain, and upon the soul of the victim a pitiful bondage to a universe of horror. With due apology to the innocents who suffered and condemnation for the wicked who committed heinous acts of bloodletting, the following cases are now revealed, noting that some of the spirits mentioned in this section remain terribly unsettled, their quest for justice still unresolved.

The House That Hated Men
Casebook Entry #23

Date of Entry:
November 9, 1972

Supernatural Category:
Haunted House/Murder/Suicide

The old, termite-infested, plantation-style cottage was located in the middle of a residential block in Mo'ili'ili, one of the last remaining remnants of the days when the district was rice and taro farms, piggeries and lotus ponds. Set in the middle of several two-story cinder-block apartment buildings situated on all four sides, the house was nearly impossible to see from any of the surrounding sidewalks. A narrow gravel path wound its way past the modern structures to provide access to this ghost of old Kamo'ili'ili, as the area was known when the cottage was built. The ill-kept, weed-filled yard in front of the home was unusually expansive considering the premium on space in the neighborhood, and a nearby huge mango tree provided much-needed shade on those sweltering Mo'ili'ili days. Several tall coconut trees, which towered over the house and neighboring apartment buildings, served as the only visual marker of the old cottage surviving below in the middle of a concrete jungle.

The realty agent informed us when we moved into the house that the owners were planning to sell the property as soon as possible for a condominium project slated for the block. For students at the University of Hawai'i at Manoa, a short-term rental was ideal. None of us had any intention to live in the dilapidated old house more than a couple of semesters. Our immediate concern was the rent, which was a phenomenally inexpensive $125 a month! Divided among the four of us, that meant we would individually have to pay, including utilities, about $35 a month. As a struggling graduate student at the university, earning about $250 a month as a teaching assistant, this was an unbeatable deal.

We therefore didn't mind the less-than-mint condition of the cottage. For $35 a month I could easily overlook the termite-eaten window sills, the doors that drooped on their hinges, the small hole in the kitchen wall near the sink, and the plumbing that was evidently installed not long after the invention of pipes and flushing toilets. The roof didn't leak too badly and there was enough space for four roommates to share each of the two bedrooms comfortably. The bathroom, with a tub rigged up with a makeshift shower head, was situated between the bedrooms. The parlor wasn't large but our coffee table was, after all, only a giant, wooden electrical wiring spool which was turned on its side in the middle of the room. The kitchen was set off in a separate room entered through the parlor. An exterior side door provided outside entrance to the kitchen.

Moving in wasn't difficult for any of us since we had virtually no furniture, save for our creative "coffee table." I purchased my first *futon* which I placed on the floor in the corner of my bedroom. My roommate, Jerry O'Connell, a surfer from Southern California, obtained an old metal army cot that he set up in the other corner. The other bedroom was shared by a recently discharged Vietnam War veteran named Howie Greenberg and my best friend in the world, Gary Tokunaga, a *"kotonk"* or "mainland" Japanese American from Los Angeles, who accompanied me in my big adventure to Hawai'i. Gary had found the other two roommates, located the cheap cottage and negotiated all of the arrangements. An unusually tall Japanese American (he was over six feet tall) and enormously handsome, he moved through this world with absolute confidence, attracting the weaker and less-sure organisms of his species to him like a human magnet. I was one of those fear-bound souls who enjoyed walking in his radiant path.

It was still the first week of our occupancy in our new rickety cottage when I awoke one morning about 8:00 AM. Jerry had not yet moved into the house, so I had slept alone in my room, which had already become warm from the September morning sun. I entered the bathroom to use the toilet and take a shower before going off to school. My first class that morning wasn't until 10:00 AM. The door to Howie and Gary's bedroom was slightly ajar, as I sat down on the toilet to read a magazine and "take care of business." I knew that Gary had spent the night at his girlfriend's house and Howie had gone to work at the supermarket at 6:00 AM. I thought I was alone in the house, until it became obvious to me that Howie must have overslept. Inside his bedroom, through the slight opening of the door, I could hear him in bed, the mattress springs squeaking. He must not have been feeling well, I decided, since his breathing was usually raspy and deep. The heavy, slow breathing of someone with asthma continued, the bed springs squeaking, as I took a shower and prepared to go to campus.

Just before I left, I went back to the bathroom, concerned that Howie may need some medicine or food if he was taking the day off with his head cold. Not wanting to intrude, I stood at the crack of his bedroom door and called out.

"Howie? You want something from the store? Are you okay? It's almost 9 o'clock!"

Howie didn't answer. In the room I heard the breathing quicken and the springs squeak more loudly as if he was turning over. I pushed the door open a little further and again asked Howie if he needed anything from the store. Again, he didn't answer, as I pushed the door back further, gently stepping into the room.

It is difficult to describe in words the feeling that enveloped me as I took one step into that room. I can only compare it to opening the ice compartment of a refrigerator, when the ice cold air drifts on to your skin, chilling it with slightly visible frigid vapors. Something moved out of Howie's room that was ice cold, sending shivers down my spine as I stopped dead in my tracks, trembling. If I hadn't known better, I would have thought Howie had left the air conditioner on all night at its lowest temperature. Only there was no air conditioner in his room, and the windows were all open, allowing the warmth of the September morning full access. No wonder he wasn't feeling well, I thought. He had been sleeping in a freezer.

Howie's bed was located in a corner of the room which was behind the door. To awaken him, I had to walk into the room to look around the door. As I did so, the cold air seemed to intensify, as I gazed down upon Howie all bundled up under his sheets and bedding, laying in a curled position. The covers were over his head, as he slightly moved on the bed, the springs continuing their rusty squeaking. Poor Howie was shivering. The raspy breathing under the bedding continued unabated, becoming more intense.

"Howie, you better get up. It's 9 o'clock."

I reached down to tap his legs, clearly outlined under the covers. As I did so, the bedding gently slid off the bed, revealing that no one was in it. Howie, I learned later, had gone to work at 6:00 AM. I was alone in the cottage. The breathing stopped, the springs ceased squeaking, the air warmed, and I fled from the house.

When Gary and I met later that day, I immediately told him what had happened. With all the confidence that I always entrusted to him, he laughed and suggested that perhaps our house was haunted. He had not told this incident to any of us yet, but the first night that he had moved into the house, he had encountered a "ghost." He had been with his girlfriend in his bedroom when at about 1:00 AM they both heard footfalls in the parlor. Believing that perhaps I or one of the other roommates was moving into the house, he got up to give a hand with the luggage. However, when he looked into the parlor, there was no one there and the sounds of the footfalls ceased. Thinking it was his imagination, he went back into the bedroom, when they both heard it again—the distinctive sound of someone walking in the parlor. Again, he took a quick look, only to find the room dark and empty. After the second incident, he turned his phonograph up so loud that, if there had been anymore footsteps, he wouldn't have been able to hear them!

That night, Gary, Howie and I gathered in the bedroom to await what we anticipated to be the footfalls of our unseen house companion. Just after 1:00 AM, we all heard the steps in the parlor which Gary had earlier described. It sounded like someone wearing heavy boots pacing evenly through the room. Dashing to the bedroom door, we looked into the room which was clearly empty, except for our makeshift coffee table and some *zabuton* strewn about the floor. I cannot say that I heard these footfalls on a regular basis, but, if all of us went into Gary's bedroom after midnight and kept deathly still, on several occasions we would hear the tread upon the old wooden floors.

Skeptics of course pronounced the footfalls as the wood in the floor shrinking in the cool of the evening. Old houses are prone to many peculiar noises, as anyone who has ever lived in such a structure will be the first to verify. Even now, trying to recall over the years precisely what they sounded like, it would not have been incorrect to suggest that the same sounds could be made from the simple creaking of wood. Why the creaking occurred only after a certain hour is a question I leave to the scientists.

Since Gary seemed greatly amused by our resident ghost, inviting his many friends and acquaintances over to the cottage to "try the spirit," I followed his example and even took to bragging about the fact that I lived in a haunted house. After all, I often boasted to myself, hadn't I studied the paranormal since I was a child? Wasn't I the "expert" on such matters? Of course, my personal experiences up to that point had been extremely limited, my knowledge confined to books. "Aren't you frightened?" some of my new local friends asked.

"Of course not," I answered, armed with my academic research. "No ghost ever hurt anyone in the history of supernatural encounters." I had read that line somewhere in a book on the occult and I repeated it as often as needed. It was a stupid, stupid sentence that had no validity in the world of Hawai'i's supernatural, a world through whose threshold I was unknowingly taking my first steps.

The months passed briskly as the excitement of the haunted cottage faded to be replaced with the fascination I was experiencing in discovering the diverse world of Honolulu in 1971. During the day, the campus of the University of Hawai'i was a vibrant setting for impassioned students and new movements as an awakening spirit of ethnic pride and political awareness shattered the calm of Manoa. My evenings were filled with long drinking sessions at the old Kuhio Grill on King Street where the beer, *sashimi,* fried shrimp and bull flowed freely. Everyone was falling in and out of love, as the little cottage in Mo'ili'ili began to radiate as a center for the counterculture which Gary Tokunaga seemed to embody. Our hair grew longer, as perhaps also did our vices.

It was during the month of January 1972 that our ghostly "friend" returned with full vengeance to our cottage. I was spending the night alone in the house, since my other three roommates had all found various other friends at whose homes they would frequently "crash." At about 3:00 AM I was awakened by what I assumed was an intruder in our house—someone evidently who had lost their mind and was attempting to tear the house apart! They had gotten into the kitchen and were slamming the cupboard doors so viciously that the dishes inside were falling and smashing. Then the intruder was opening and shutting the utensil drawers, throwing the forks, spoons and knives all over the kitchen. These sounds were extremely distinct and remain in my memory, unfaded, over two and one-half decades later.

Terrified that this intruder may be armed with a weapon, I grabbed an old baseball bat that Jerry had left in the bedroom, turned on all the lights in my bedroom and the parlor, and started shouting out threats of calling the police. I stood in the parlor, Louisville Slugger poised to smash the head of anyone who exited the kitchen, screaming my head off to get out of the house. Inside the pitch-dark kitchen, the intruder continued to tear the cupboards and utensil drawers apart, destroying our dishes, pots, pans and kitchen implements. The pounding was thunderous, as the kitchen walls shook from the assault. Despite all my threats, the intruder refused to leave, and never entered the parlor.

Finally, desperate to get rid of the assailant, but trembling with fear, I put one hand into the kitchen, groping for the light switch on the wall. I was hoping that this madman would flee out the back door once the lights were turned on brightly. I moved my left hand around on the inside kitchen wall, praying to find the switch, while I held the bat high with my right hand, ready to clobber anyone in the kitchen.

Just as I found the switch, the unseen intruder found my hand. His grip was powerful as he squeezed my fingers tightly in an ice cold clench. I let out a scream that must have been heard in Makiki, as the baseball bat came down violently just in the place where someone must have been standing to have grabbed my hand. The bat hit the floor with a loud thud as I lunged back into the parlor, my fingers first sweeping up and flicking on the light switch. Ready to be pounced upon by whoever was in the kitchen, I was scrambling to run out the front door, when suddenly all the pounding noises in the kitchen stopped. Gasping for breath, I tried to calm down and looked back into the kitchen, hoping to see the back door open and the intruder gone.

Amazingly, I found the kitchen wholly empty of human presence and in perfect peace and order. No cupboard was open. All utensil drawers were shut. No dishes were disturbed or out of place. Every fork, spoon and knife was in its correct little compartment in the drawer. The back door was latched from the inside and the doorknob locked. No one had been in the room, although I swore that an icy hand had touched mine when I had dared to turn the lights on to what I thought had been a scene of mayhem. I again fled from the house that night and sought shelter at a friend's home in Manoa Valley. Unbeknownst to me in 1972, I had experienced what I would later learn was an aural poltergeist—the sounds of moving objects although the objects themselves are stationary.

Breathing and walking ghosts seemed innocuous enough, but even Gary agreed that, when they start tearing the kitchen apart, the time had come for an exorcism. I was a novice at that time in supernatural matters, and new to the Islands. So finding someone to bless the house was not easy. Gary agreed to pursue the local Japanese community for an exorcist, while I would try the University of Hawai'i. Since in the early 1970s there was a large student interest in witchcraft and astrology, one afternoon I attended a "psychic fair" gathering in Hemenway Lounge, the student center, and innocently asked if anyone knew of someone who did exorcisms.

"Oh, I'm learning to do that!" an attractive, young, local Portuguese woman answered. "I'm very psychic and have helped many of my friends rid their apartments of unwanted spirits." Since a beggar at this point could not be a chooser, I gave her our address, as well as instructions to find the house, and made arrangements to meet her that afternoon at 5:00 PM.

By 5:30 PM I was still waiting for our exorcist and decided that she had either changed her mind or had become lost. I was wrong on both scores. Our "psychic cleanser" was trembling, immobilized on the sidewalk on a Mo'ili'ili street just at the gravel footpath that led to the site of our little cottage. I found her when I had finally gone out to the street to look for her automobile.

"I can't walk into that area," she said when she saw me. "It's evil. Something evil is in there."

I explained that was why we had summoned her, to clear the house of its ghostly presence.

"You don't understand, it's evil," she repeated. "I am new at this. I've never sensed anything so vicious. I'm not sure I can do this."

I reassured her that she had to start somewhere in her career as a house exorcist. This was as good as any other place to get good experience. Despite her great reluctance, I cajoled her just a little bit, with just a gentle push upon the shoulders, to walk the pathway to the cottage. It must have taken her 30 minutes to walk 10 yards, inching her way to the house while trembling as if her body was in an arctic wind. If this was an act, I thought, this woman was very, very good.

When I finally got her into the house, she immediately walked into the kitchen, telling me that the spirit's presence was strongest here. I instantly regretted telling her about the occurrences which had taken place in the house, since she was obviously using this knowledge to convince me of her powers. The assault in the kitchen, the most powerful manifestation in the house, was a fact of which she was fully aware. I swore at that time, if I ever restage a psychic investigation, the "exorcist" would be given no prior information on the manifestations.

Gaining more confidence, the young woman then walked right up to a cupboard which contained the ironing board, pulled it open and pointed to a small higher shelf where detergent was kept.

"Your spirit is right up there!" she declared.

"In that little space?" I was surprised, since the entity seemed to be larger and more powerful than something squeezed into that little area.

"It is concentrated" was her simple reply.

I silently laughed at the thought of concentrated spirits. I knew, of course, of concentrated orange juice, but I was unaware of the process for ghosts. Over the years the notion that a spirit during the day would concentrate itself in a tiny space, like a jewelry box or a corner shelf, became increasingly evident to me as both spirit-seers, as well as occult books, described such concentrations. The spirit would be able to take many forms when it wished, but during nonactivity would "concentrate" itself in one small place.

"Well, get rid of it," I then encouraged the exorcist. "Whether concentrated or not, it is unwelcome."

"I can't," she then said. "It's evil. It hates you. And it hates your roommates. It can't stand men, and you've brought four of them into the house."

"It hates men?"

"You better leave," she then advised me. "It will kill you when it gets the chance." With that final proclamation, the young woman dashed out the side door, back to her car without further explanation. Except for an occasional nod of recognition on campus, she refused to ever speak to me again. She of course never again visited our little cottage, and I wouldn't be surprised if she even now continues to avoid the neighborhood where the house once stood.

Later that night the four of us discussed the warning that I had been given. Moving out of a house that, other than the manifestations, had become a very exciting place seemed unreasonable. Plus, the low rent would be impossible to find at any other location near the university. She was, after all, a novice and could have been totally off-base. In the last week, our unseen resident had not made any further visits, not even the nocturnal walking. As long as none of us had to stay alone overnight in the house, we agreed that staying on would be just fine. Gary promised to get the name of a local Japanese *odaisan* or healer/exorcist to try to bless the house.

Two weeks later, at about 1:00 AM, I was driving my 1957 Chevrolet station wagon, which I had purchased for only $100, through a major intersection in the McCully area. I entered the intersection with the green light, going fully within the speed limit. Jerry was sitting next to me in the front seat. I had just picked him up at a friend's house and was bringing him back to our cottage. As I was about to clear the intersection, I suddenly heard the sound of grinding metal, as my car began to lift from the pavement. I can recall the smell of burning rubber and metal which filled my nostrils, as the world seemed to spin uncontrollably and the grinding metal turned to screeching sounds that filled the still city air. The swirling, turning car skidded on its roof across the intersection as I clutched the steering wheel. An explosion of glass was followed by the scream of Jerry, who had vanished from the front passenger seat. I have no memory of how I got out of the demolished station wagon, but in the next few moments I found myself standing in the middle of the intersection, surrounded by the strewn contents of my car. Jerry was in the back compartment of the station wagon, his leg bleeding from a light cut, but otherwise in good condition. I was completely untouched, although my car was "totaled."

Another car with its front hood smashed like an accordion was silently stopped at the place where it had run the red light and collided with the tail end of my vehicle. I surveyed the scene almost as if I wasn't a victim of an accident, but an astral observer detached from the confusion, sirens and swarming police. My car was parked on its roof inside a flower shop located on the corner, the large bay window shattered by my station wagon. To this day, I am puzzled at how I survived that hit-and-run collision without a scratch. Jerry went to the hospital and was later released with just a few stitches on his leg to stop the bleeding.

Two days later Howie lost control of his sports car on the H-1 freeway near Punahou Street, slamming into the divider. The impact of the collision ripped off his fender, sheared the car along the length of the left side, tearing off the driver's door and rear fender. Howie's upper body was dragged along the wire fence of the median strip, causing the thick leather jacket which he was fortunately wearing to be shredded like fringe. He was untouched and walked home unassisted from the freeway wreckage of his "totaled" automobile. Three weeks later Gary plunged the front of his Volkswagen into a huge tree in Nu'uanu Valley along Nu'uanu Pali Drive. On one of the hairpin turns, the bolt that attached the steering wheel to the shaft had suddenly become loose and his uncontrolled car slammed right into the tree. He was also unhurt, but very shaken.

With three car accidents destroying our automobiles within a four-week period, the effort to find a Japanese *odaisan* intensified. Finally, Gary was able to find a small Japanese mystical sect located in Kalihi willing to do blessings for nonmembers. The old sensei or teacher of the sect who visited our Mo'ili'ili cottage arrived in his ceremonial robes, toting a small briefcase in which he carried his special objects, incense, prayer book, prayer beads, and other items required to bless the house. He spoke only a smattering of English, and I was at that time wholly unfamiliar with the ceremonies of Japanese healers or exorcists. As he laid out his paraphernalia on our "coffee table," he suddenly stopped, walked to the various corners of the parlor, closed his eyes, meditated and finally spoke.

"Too much sexu here," he said in English. "Better you leave. Many spiritsu in Mo'ili'ili."

Although his English wasn't extensive enough to fully explain to us, his younger, local Japanese-American student translated. The spirit that lived in this house had been very pious. It was a very disturbed man who despised sex and who saw us as an intrusion into his home. We had brought many girlfriends into the house, the *odaisan* explained. This sexual activity had greatly disturbed the spirit which was now seeking to destroy us. His blessing could help, he further explained, but would need to be often repeated. And the sex, he offered as advice, should stop in this cottage.

The blessing was performed and, for a while, nothing of consequence or an untoward nature happened to any of us. No manifestations of the spirit were ever heard again in the house, and no further car accidents took place, although most of us were relegated to bus, bike or foot. Maybe we would have lived there as long as our landlord would have allowed, had it not been for the tragedy that happened one night to Jerry. It was that late evening that I became convinced that ghost stories were not only oddly fun and "chicken skin," but very deadly.

I had been out with friends at the Kuhio Grill and returned to the cottage at 2:00 AM in the morning. It was April 1972 and Jerry had been staying in the house for a few days with a high fever and strep throat. A generally happy-go-lucky guy, he had had very little interest in the ghost visitations, preferring his surfing and pakalolo to preternatural beings. He was the last person in the world who I would have believed had any deep-down anxieties or Angst. So, when I entered the bathroom that night after returning home, I was shocked to find blood all over the shower curtain, on the mirror and door. What in the hell had Jerry done?

I pulled the curtain back and there he was, sitting fully clothed in the empty bathtub, his eyes wide open, staring at me. His arms were turned up and were both scratched from top to bottom with shallow wounds from a razor blade which now laid on the tub at the fingers of his right hand. He had evidently first cut up his arms and smeared the blood all over the bathroom, on the mirror, walls, doors and curtain before sitting down in the tub and finishing off the job with two deeper slits to the arteries in both wrists. Jerry's thick, red blood had formed into a pool in the tub and flowed gently into the drain, where it trickled slowly down in a tiny circular motion, quietly feeding the pipes of our old cottage home.

We all moved after the suicide of Jerry O'Connell, each of us going in different directions. One afternoon, before we finally had all our things out of the cottage, I did ask the manager of the apartment building next door if he had known anything about the house. He was a debonair Frenchman in his late fifties with an excellent, paper-thin mustache right out of the films of the 1930s. He spoke with a thick French accent and had a hint of cognac on his breath.

"Yes, many people have lived in that house," he told me. "In the 10 years I have managed this apartment, I have seen many come and go."

I asked if there had been any other tragedies like the one which had taken place during our residency. He wasn't sure if there had been any suicides in the house, he continued, but there had been many fights and the police had made many visits to either arrest the tenants for violation of the peace or to stop a disturbance.

"Some nights, when the house was empty with no tenants," he volunteered, "my son and I have heard dishes smashing and cupboards slamming. Very odd, because no one is renting. They should tear that old place down."

They did finally tear it down. Within six months of our leaving the old cottage, the building was completely razed. Two years later a towering condominium replaced the grounds and the surrounding apartments that had all been demolished for the sake of progress. I often wondered what had become of that dashing old Frenchman with the pencil-thin mustache and his son.

Ten years after all these events, in the course of doing historical research on Mo'ili'ili for a planned walking tour, I interviewed some long-time residents about the various families and people who had lived in the area. Many of the interviewees had grown up in the area when it was still rice and taro farms and had vivid memories of the early Chinese and Japanese independent farmers who pioneered these industries at the turn of the century. One of the old-timers recalled how one of these farmers had a cottage which many years later still stood in the middle of an apartment complex. Suspecting that this was the very cottage which I had once occupied as a young graduate student at the University of Hawai'i, I pressed for more information.

He had been a hermit-like, old Japanese man, the interviewee continued, who was a very peculiar fellow. There were all types of rumors that had been circulated about him, most of it very vicious. The children used to say that he was kichigai or crazy because he had no friends, rarely stepped off his property, and never got married. The parents whispered whenever they talked about the hermit, some suggesting that he was some kind of molester of boys. The children were always warned to stay away from that old man's house and never to play on his property.

"What finally happened to him?" I asked.

"One night a neighbor went over to his cottage to complain about the old man's dogs getting out and attacking his kids. He talked to the old man at the side kitchen door. Suddenly, the old guy went crazy and attacked the neighbor. There was a terrible fight in the kitchen, when that crazy old man horribly stabbed the neighbor to death."

"Wow! In the kitchen? What happened then?"

"The old man went back into his bathroom and committed suicide in his tub. Real Japanese style, yeah? He used a knife. Cut open his guts. Real hara kiri. Most times in those days, people used rope to hang themselves. Today, maybe pills, yeah? But that old man used a knife. After that, we used to call that house the obake house, although I don't know about any ghosts there. That was some place."

No one had ever told us about the murder and suicide that had taken place inside our little cottage. Now there was only Gary to inform, but by then he was living thousands of miles away from Hawai'i. Howie was gone. One year after we had moved from the Mo'ili'ili cottage, he became entangled in a love affair that turned sour. Plagued by dark memories of Vietnam, as well as a growing drug dependency, one morning he put a bullet through his right temple. That left only two of us alive who had once lived in the house that hated men. And that house was nothing more than a bitter memory blended with the sweeter glimmering images of another generation, of the days of innocent youth and unattained ideals, of Kuhio Grill and *sashimi,* before the search on a blood-stained path into a secret realm of evil.

A Faceless Woman on the Old Pali Road
Casebook Entry #1467

Date of Entry:
March 15, 1992

Supernatural Category:
Haunted Campus/Restless Spirit/Faceless Woman/Psychic Synchronicity

The bloodcurdling scream of the New Zealand psychic shattered the still air of the No Ka 'Oi Elementary School campus as a small group of us ran in the direction of the banshee wail. I had been escorting a group of about seven psychics from Australia and New Zealand to the haunted school campus in an effort to make contact with the variety of Hawaiian ghosts who were terrorizing the staff and students. Among the psychics was my friend and frequent guide into the world of the supernatural, Glennys MacKay, who had earlier that evening suddenly felt inside her head the spiritual pain of hundreds of ancient spirits killed with heavy clubs during a ferocious battle. These spirits, she claimed, were causing the disturbances on the campus which included sacks of flour thrown about a cafeteria otherwise locked and secured, giant footprints appearing in the flour and pools of watered-down blood. On another occasion, the police reported hearing drumming inside the cafeteria. All these occurrences and more were described in detail in the case of "The Exorcised Campus" published in *The Obake Files*.

The screams which now emanated from the far side of the campus, however, were wholly unrelated to the ancient battle which had caused the paranormal activities within the cafeteria. Those screams were from a far more modern and innocent victim of a terrible crime whose memory had moved like an ebb tide over time, slowly receding in the heart until, with the force of a tsunami, it burst back that night into the present.

Running across the grassy field at midnight in response to the psychic's screams, I was at first worried that neighbors would call the police. It literally sounded as if someone was being horribly murdered. When we all arrived a little out of breath at the scene of the disturbance, the New Zealand woman was laying on the damp lawn, writhing about on the grass almost like a snake. Her boyfriend, who also claimed to have a spiritual sixth sense, tried to talk to the spirit that had possessed the young woman. Her head was turning wildly back and forth, as her gaping mouth uttered tortured shrieks that would have awakened even the dead. Both legs were squirming as her torso twisted about, sometimes jerking up and then collapsing back to the lawn. I wasn't certain what was happening, and at first believed the New Zealand woman was undergoing some type of epileptic fit.

"What's going on?" I nervously asked, expecting to hear police sirens any minute. "Should I call an ambulance?"

"She fell right on this spot," her boyfriend soothingly explained. "A spirit has possessed her. She's perfectly safe."

"Margaret is a trance medium who receives the spirit inside her body," Glennys quickly explained to me. "She's very experienced at this. The spirit is moving inside of her."

"Ohhhhhhhh, noooooo!" the spirit inside of Margaret now screamed, for the first time using intelligible words. "I don't want to do this! Oh, please don't do this! God help me!"

These words were followed by a strangled, gargled cry as if her throat was tightening. Something was trying to keep the spirit from talking to us by suddenly choking the psychic. Then her legs were jerked apart wildly as her back flew up and fell violently to the ground. The spirit's breathing lowered to more guttural tones. It kept repeating over and over again that it didn't want to do this, it didn't want to do this. The psychic's legs trembled and tried to cross themselves, but were again thrust widely open.

"Oh, my God," Glennys muttered, "the poor soul is being raped."

The other psychics stood silently about their friend, evidently unable to give her any assistance. A few were in deep meditation, one stepped away and looked trance-like into space, while Glennys crouched over the writhing form and prayed with her eyes closed tightly. The boyfriend continued to soothe the psychic's hand as the intensity of the attack went on unabated.

It is difficult to describe how nauseated I felt, watching a poor woman physically attacked during a heinous crime, standing right over her and being entirely helpless to stop the assault. The sobbing tears, the begging and the guttural cries, I knew, were the genuine horrified emotions of the victim, not a play-act by the psychic. Occasionally Glennys spoke out to the spirit to coax it into the light, to depart from this world into the next. But the rape was just a prelude to a torrent of terror that the young victim needed to tell us.

Her body and legs finally, for a moment, stopped jerking on the grass, as a pitiful deep sobbing of shame and pain began to emanate from the throat of the psychic. She finally seemed to be calming down, as I prayed that this little disturbing episode was over. But the devil who had just sexually assaulted the spirit now seemed to tie something around her throat which was tightened as more sounds of choking emanated from the throat of the psychic.

"He's murdering her now," the boyfriend said, still calm in the midst of this madness. "I see him with a rope tied around her neck, pulling it into a tight knot. The spirit is reliving her strangulation." He caressed one of the psychic's hands as her body communicated to us the murder of the spirit, recreating her last horrible gasping, desperate efforts to suck in air. The body of the psychic then went totally limp, her eyes closed, and she assumed the posture of a corpse.

I waited for what seemed an eternity for the young woman to awaken from her dead state. I secretly prayed that she was simply fabricating all this to make a big spiritual impression on me with an extraordinary demonstration of her so-called powers. No one else seemed at all fazed by her demise, but they patiently waited for the psychic to awaken from her trance. However, instead of opening her eyes and sitting up, her right leg slowly started to stiffen, as the right side of her body seemed to also become rigid. It was as if a slow paralysis was creeping up her flesh until it reached the neck, lower jaw and, finally, the face.

"Look," Glennys explained in fascination, "the body is actually undergoing rigor mortis. The spirit is showing us what happened hours after she died."

Unbelievably, the New Zealand psychic's entire body slowly went into a rigid form that appeared to this untrained layman's eye to be a several-days-old corpse. Under the flashlight that I now held tight on her upper body, I saw that her facial features also began to alter slightly, the lower portion of the mouth and cheeks slowly becoming stretched taut like a rubber band. It seemed that, in addition to being a psychic, this young New Zealand woman must have also been a facial contortionist. The lower features of her face gradually seemed literally to transform into a flat nothingness. The mouth, cheeks and even nose were hardly distinguishable. The upper portion of her face, however, seemed unaffected by the paralysis. During the entire creeping rigor mortis process, her eyes were tightly closed. But when her body was finally completely frozen and the lower face contorted, the eyelids of both eyes slowly began to open together like tiny shutters of a camera widening the lens. They inched their way open until both eyes were fully revealed, the pupils like hollow tunnels into emptiness. Then the eyeballs began moving forward, as if literally trying to pop out of their sockets. When they extended as far as humanly possible, the eyes kept that grotesque posture for about a minute. It seemed as if they were transfixed directly on me, and an uneasy shiver was released through my own flesh.

Finally, the body of the psychic relaxed, the eyes closed and a ripple of life went through her legs and arms. She had not breathed during the paralysis, so now a healthy, deep intake of the fresh evening air seemed to revitalize her. The other psychics who had been in deep meditations also seemed to come back to reality, while the boyfriend and Glennys helped the exhausted New Zealand woman sit up.

The entire episode on the lawn must have lasted over 20 minutes. Incredibly, despite all of her terrorized screams, no police ever arrived at the campus. Maybe this was a nightly occurrence at No Ka ʻOi Elementary School, I thought, so the neighbors never bothered to dial 911! We assisted Margaret to her feet and her boyfriend held her by the waist as we all walked back to the cars. Someone had brought a bottle of water, which the exhausted psychic thirstily consumed. In the light of the parking lot, I noticed that Margaret, the New Zealand psychic, was much younger than I had originally thought when she was writhing on the ground. She was a pretty, full-figured woman in her mid-twenties with short blonde hair. Her Hilo Hattie muʻumuʻu was now covered with grass stains. Around her neck she wore what I assumed was some kind of crystal pendant associated with "new age" spirituality. When she put her dark, horn-rimmed glasses which had fallen off during the "possession," back on, she appeared a little bookwormish. One would not have assumed that this quite ordinary-appearing person had the fantastic ability, from childhood, to allow spirits to enter her body and relive their torturous deaths!

"I'm truly exhausted," she finally said. "This spirit was incredibly powerful and possessive. She seemed quite determined to tell us this story. I assume that a murder took place on this campus? Is this why you brought us here?"

She was looking at me, expecting a knowledgeable answer. After all, I had brought the seven of them to this campus with no explanation or preparation. To be quite honest, I always like to "test" psychics by providing absolutely no information about any alleged haunting in the area. If they are not from Hawaiʻi, I additionally make sure that they are unexposed to any history books, legends or other cultural information while in the Islands. In this way I try to keep their minds a complete *tabla rasa* or blank slate, so that any information they do give me can be appraised based upon its sacred, not profane, sources. However, this kind of violent assault upon a psychic was wholly unanticipated, considering the type of haunting that had occurred on the campus. Most of the phenomena seemed associated with ancient battles, not modern-day crimes of passion. In addition, I had no information about a murder having ever taken place upon the campus.

"I am sorry, but I don't know anything about a crime having occurred here. There were some disturbances in the cafeteria concerning drumming and other weird things, but no one mentioned to me anything about a woman being murdered."

"She wasn't a woman," the psychic then explained. "She was a young teenage girl. Maybe about 15 years old? I'm not really certain."

"I saw the man who murdered her," added the boyfriend. "I can draw his picture."

No one had a piece of clean white paper, but there was a napkin in my car that we unfolded. Carefully, the young man drew a sketch of a large male figure with a closely cropped "butch" haircut and a football jersey with the number "10." The drawing is reproduced below

A Sketch of the Murderer

I assured all of them that, if a murder had taken place at No Ka 'Oi School, then a search through the newspaper indexes would give us full information of the crime. Then we could confirm whether or not the information given to us by the psychic and her boyfriend could be verified. In addition, I suggested that I could try to call the police tomorrow and ask them if they knew anything about a rape and murder on the campus. I wasn't certain if the Honolulu Police Department would disclose that information to the public, but it wouldn't hurt to try.

Everyone was now eager to visit another haunted place about town, but, since it was after midnight and I had had more than enough of my own personal experiences that night witnessing other people being supernaturally assaulted, I strongly suggested that we return to their hotel. Glennys sensed my unease, aware that I was a true "ghost chicken." She convinced the others that we had indeed had enough for one evening. Margaret, however, urged me to take them to a restaurant so that they could at least get some "nourishment."

I immediately began to think of places serving food that were still open and which were absolutely free from any kind of supernatural presence. What could be safer than Zippy's? I thought. Driving back into town from the Pearl City district, we pulled into Zippy's on King Street near Washington Intermediate School. The waitresses rearranged some tables and we all sat down together to consume a few bowls of saimin, a couple of burgers and a bowl of chili.

Halfway through the meal, a young man walked by the table, stopped and asked if I was the "chicken skin guy." He had forgotten my name, but went on to tell me how much he had enjoyed one of the walking tours that he had taken a few years before in downtown Honolulu.

"Hey," he added with a big smile, "it was really scary, yeah?"

"You thought the tour was scary?" Margaret said, hardly looking up from her bowl of saimin. "You should have been with us tonight. We made communication with a woman who was raped and murdered at No Ka 'Oi School."

Now bug-eyed, the young man sat down with us at the table to listen to Margaret and a few of the others share briefly the events which had happened that evening. The young man sat silently listening to the chatter of several people speaking at once, trying to give out details simultaneously.

"That is so cool," he said, as he excused himself once the tale had been told. "I gotta go back to my table, but that was really interesting. Nice meeting you folks."

Giving me a quick, local-style handshake, the young man walked off to join his family seated on the other side of the restaurant. We were just about finishing our meal when we were interrupted again, this time by an older Hawaiian woman perhaps in her mid-fifties, who politely asked if she could talk with us. She introduced herself as Anna Kalilikane, the grandmother of the young man to whom we had just related our strange experiences at No Ka 'Oi School.

"Is it true that you just tonight made contact with a young girl murdered at the campus?" She was slightly nervous as she asked the question, for I noticed that her hands were trembling.

"Yes," I answered. "What your grandson said is true."

"My God," she muttered. "Janette has come back! Oh my, after all these years!"

Through her tears she explained that all afternoon she had been thinking about Janette Lum, her childhood friend who, in 1951 at the age of 14, was kidnapped after classes from the intermediate school located right next to No Ka 'Oi School. For over 40 years she had kept this trauma buried so deep in her heart, that she thought that she had completely erased all vestiges of its memory. Anna had been only 13 years old at the time of the kidnapping, and who would have ever thought that such an horrific event could happen in peaceful, little Aiea town? For years she had refused to even speak to Janette's family, although they all lived not more than a few blocks from one another.

In fact, she hadn't communicated with the family until that very morning. She had been in the supermarket doing her weekly shopping, when a woman stopped her in the aisle with a broad smile and friendly greeting. Not knowing who the person was, but trying to be friendly since she obviously knew her, Anna carried on with polite chitchat until, with dread, she heard the woman use the name "Janette." This was Janette's youngest sister, who had been only seven years old at the time of the crime. Anna had not talked to her all these years, and now they confronted each other in the supermarket in friendly banter.

A flood of repressed childhood memories overwhelmed Anna, as her knees nearly gave way underneath her. She nearly fainted now, hearing the name "Janette Lum" after four decades. Fortunately, she was able to get through the conversation as quickly as possible, excused herself saying that she had an afternoon appointment, left her groceries in the shopping cart and rushed home. All afternoon she had sat on her living room couch pondering what to do. Should she seek some kind of counseling? Perhaps she should face the fears and anxieties she had consciously buried as a little girl.

"Imagine my shock," she went on to explain, "when my grandson came back to our table a few minutes ago and told us what you folks had just experienced. I couldn't believe it."

Glennys is a registered nurse and a master at comforting those who have had spiritual traumas. She put her arm around Anna and explained how the spirit of her friend must have known that all of us would meet later that evening—that she gave us this message as a way to comfort Anna, to let her know that she must accept what happened, remember her friend and go on with her own life stronger. This was no coincidence, Glennys said, but an example of "psychic synchronicity," or "meaningful coincidences."

In my life as a collector of ghost stories, the notion of "meaningful coincidences" has become a pattern that I often look for. This hadn't been the first time that a series of events took place when, looking back over them, you realized that they had happened for a purpose. Usually that purpose was linked to some unsettled spirit whose long-forgotten existence had aroused it from its slumber to reach out from the grave to communicate with its loved ones. Often my work had unwittingly served as the conduit for that communication to take place. Now, here in Zippy's Restaurant, one more moment of "synchronicity" was dramatically taking place.

We didn't need to coax Anna to tell us the full story of what had happened to Janette Lum. She told it like a 40-year-old secret that she needed to confess to someone. Every afternoon, Janette, Anna and their other friends would stay after classes to do homework in the intermediate school's library. Janette was an excellent student and was always conscientious about completing her assignments with 110 percent effort. That particular day, Anna and the others decided to leave the school early so that they could rendezvous with a group of boys who always "talked story" at a small "mama and papa-san" store in Aiea. Janette would finish her work and join them later.

Janette never showed up at the store. Later that night her parents called Anna's parents to find out where Janette had gone. The school librarian said that she had left the campus at 4:00 PM. She never got home. Her parents called the police and a search was made for the missing girl. All of the parents in the neighborhood joined in a posse to scour the Aiea district and to search the sugar cane fields. Janette was never found.

One afternoon a week later a group of teenagers hiking and exploring along the Old Pali Road in Kailua came upon the remains of a body that had been dumped in the bushes along a desolate part of that jungle-encased roadway. The police were called, and an autopsy revealed that the badly decomposed corpse was indeed little Janette Lum. Dental records confirmed the identity. Further examination revealed that she had been sexually assaulted and then strangled to death with a piece of rope that was well-known to Anna and her friends. It was the jump rope that Janette used to play with when she walked to and from school.

For months the murder of Janette Lum was an unsolved case that left Aiea shocked and parents terrified. Children no longer walked to or from school unescorted, and most parents put a curfew on their kids, making sure they were at home long before sunset. No one knew if the killer had been some crazed stranger who had snatched Janette off the street or possibly someone with hom she was acquainted.

Finally, an arrest was made and a full confession given by an older teenage boy who had actually known Janette. He was a good friend of one of her cousins and he had often visited the Lum home. The afternoon of the crime, he had shown up outside of her school in his "hot rod" to impress her. He offered her a ride home and then suggested they take a ride over to the beaches on the Windward side. She was hesitant, but he told her that it would be all right. They played on the beach at Kane'ohe Bay for a while, but by sunset Janette was anxious to get home. It was already nightfall by the time he was driving along the Old Pali Road. When he reached a heavily wooded area on the road, he suddenly pulled his car over. He tried to "make out" with her, but she was very frightened. She tried to stop him, but he overpowered her. He told the police that when he raped her, she was screaming so loud that he finally used the jump rope to silence her. He never intended to murder her. Frightened at what he had done, he threw her body into the bushes and drove home. He was glad that he was finally caught so that he could confess.

"Did you know what this boy looked like?" the New Zealand psychic's boyfriend asked when Anna finished her story.

"Yes, we all knew him. He was from townside, but he was always at Janette's house. Maybe it was because we had known him that I was so terrified by what had happened. I vowed never, ever to think of my best friend again."

"What did he look like?" Glennys asked, gently pressing Anna to remember.

"He was a very big, Portuguese-Hawaiian boy who went to McKinley High School. I think he must have been an athlete, because he was always wearing his football shirt to impress us girls that he was one of the McKinley Tigers."

A football jersey. For the fourth time that night my skin was swept with a tingling sensation as the hair on my arms stood up.

"Did he look like this?" the boyfriend said, holding the napkin with the crude drawing out to Anna. Her glassy, reddened eyes now let loose a sad flood of tears as she nodded her head in agreement. There was no doubt in any of our minds that a poor innocent soul had finally been able to touch the world of the living to let the healing process begin.

The days and weeks passed in the normal routines that consume so much of our lives with mediocrity, when the final chapter in the case of the murder of Janette Lum was written. One evening, as a group of people gathered about me after one of my downtown walking tours, a young couple asked if they could speak privately to me. We sat down on the steps of old KawaiaHa'o Church so that they could relate to me a supernatural encounter that they had just had only a few months before.

"I know it sounds crazy, Dr. Grant," the young man said, "but my girlfriend will verify that we both saw it."

They had been parked on the Kailua side of the Old Pali Road one night, not far from where the road is now fenced off. They both enjoy ghost stories, and. since they had heard so many tales about Morgan's Corner, they thought it would be scary to drive up on the old, desolate road. So they were parked for a while "not doing anything but talking," they reassured me. I told them that I wasn't their parent and whatever they were doing up on the Old Pali Road was none of my business.

At any rate, suddenly the girlfriend, who was looking over the young man's shoulder, literally began to gag, pointing frantically over the shoulder of her boyfriend. She was so frightened that her throat had tightened, making it impossible for her to talk. He turned around to see a young girl, possibly 14 or 15 years old, skipping rope down the middle of the Old Pali Road about 20 yards behind their automobile. She was wearing a long, white dress that had flowing white sleeves. When she reached the back of their car, she stopped skipping rope and began to come down the road toward them.

"Dr. Grant," the young man said, "this girl had no feet. She was floating down the road." His girlfriend confirmed the fact that the girl had lost her lower limbs at about the kneecap. With her arms outstretched, the white-dressed phantom, who had long, black hair, floated past their automobile. As she came abreast of the car, she suddenly looked directly into the automobile at the young couple, both of whom were frozen in fear. Her face was clearly visible in a ray of moonlight that filled the road at that one place.

"Her mouth, nose, chin and cheeks were gone," the young man said emphatically. "She had no face below the eyes. But her eyes were intact and they were wide-open, almost bulging out of her skull and looking directly at me and my girlfriend."

As the vision of this partially faceless woman floated by their car, it then turned and floated directly in front of them, about two or three feet from the hood. Her body then bent slightly forward and those horrible, bulging eyes looked through the windshield at the two of them. Then as suddenly as she had appeared, she vanished.

"We got the hell out of there," he concluded, his voice trembling with fear, remembering his encounter. "And I swear that is the absolute truth."

I didn't tell the young couple that evening as they were going home that I, too, had seen the "faceless" woman with the bulging eyes. Only I hadn't seen her on the Old Pali Road. I had encountered her on a dark intermediate school campus at midnight, looking up at me from the face of a New Zealand psychic who had been my medium to the world of the undead.

As the biggest gossip in town, the story of the "faceless" woman on the Old Pali Road (without using the name of the victim), became part of my regular storytelling wherever I appeared throughout the Islands. It was one year later, after sharing the young couple's strange encounter at a presentation at Borders bookstore in Waikele, that a burly old Hawaiian man whispered something to me that I asked him to repeat, not having heard it correctly.

"That's Janette Lum, yeah?"

"How did you know that?"

"I worked on that case when I was a cop years ago. In fact, I was one of the officers who was first at the scene after the kids called in that they had found the body. I saw the corpse."

"You saw her?"

"Yeah. And that's true what those folks said they saw. The lower part of her face had been eaten away by rats and mongoose. The poor thing had no flesh below her eyes. But for some reason, her eyes were okay. Only they were rolling out of their sockets, just like they were bulging. Man, I could never forget that."

Last year I revisited the intermediate school next to the No Ka 'Oi campus with about five of my students from Hawai'i Tokai International College. It had been nearly four years since the night the New Zealand psychic had been possessed by Janette Lum, and my class had an interest in a midnight visit to a place that was alleged to be "haunted." As we walked across the campus, an air conditioner in one of the buildings started up unexpectedly, causing the students to suddenly freeze in their tracks. I laughed to myself at their temerity, as I walked on to the place where I had seen the psychic writhing on the grass. Like the night of the "possession," the air was still with the sweet scent of gardenia from a nearby plant. I was remembering the dramatic events that had taken place, when four unusual shadows on the wall of a building caught my eye.

The shadows were cylinder-shaped figures about eight feet in height that were pitch-black against the wall. They were evenly spaced, about two feet from one another along a 10-foot section of the building. The lights which created the shadows were located on a pole about 30 feet away. Curiously, there was no object between the light and the wall that could be the source of the shadows! One of my students walked up to me and I asked if he saw the shadows.

"Yeah," he answered, "what are they?" He looked around as I had done to find the source of the shadows and was puzzled when he also saw that nothing was physically standing between the light source and the wall.

Slowly, ever so slowly, the shadows then began to move on the wall, never losing their evenly spaced distance between each other. I felt my student's fingers digging into my arm, as my stomach twisted into a tight knot and adrenaline rushed through my veins. My heartbeat quickened as I watched each shadow move about 50 feet along the wall and then individually vanish into a large ti plant that had been growing outside the school building. It was an extraordinary vision which my student later verified he also had seen.

At the moment the last of these preternatural shadows vanished into the ti plant, the scream of a girl suddenly pierced the still air. The single, high-pitched cry was heard by everyone. Some of the students assumed it had come from one of the houses around the campus. No one was anywhere to be seen who could have let loose the unsettling shriek. Having little knowledge about the history of the campus or the "psychic" incident that had taken place back in 1992, the students giggled nervously and decided to return to their automobiles.

I stayed behind for a few moments alone, deciding to sit down on the very spot where the psychic had fallen. The brief single scream could have been someone in a house across the street. The shadows may have been explainable as something other than a supernatural specter. A thousand logical rationales may explain these "synchronicities" swirling about me through time. It didn't matter. Tears were pouring from the corner of my eyes as I thought of Janette Lum being murdered on a lonely wooded road, the last horrible moments of her precious little life, and the true fragility of all those things we hope for that are fine and good.

An Evil Older than Human Settlement
Casebook Entry #864

Date of Entry:
December 2, 1994

Supernatural Category:
Haunted House/Ancient Evil/Disembodied Hand

Does "Evil" exist as an independent, demonic supernatural force capable of invading the materialistic world within which most of us safely live? Are there indeed "nonhuman" spirits whose sole purpose is to wreak terror and havoc upon the human condition? Religions around the world have grappled with this moral dilemma since the dawn of time. Each of us draws our own conclusions as to whether the universe is in a cosmic struggle between forces of Good and Evil, whether the Prince of Darkness truly exists, or whether wickedness can ever exist independent of the human heart which creates it. Quite honestly, the question of the existence of "Evil" was never a theological concern that attracted much of my brain power.

That is, not until I received a telephone call one sunny morning in March 1988 from a representative of the public relations office of the Honolulu Police Department. I had known Agnes Matsushita for about a year through my interest in researching the historic crimes of old Honolulu for the McDougal crime series. Agnes was very helpful, providing old newsletters from the Honolulu Police Department that always included interviews with retired officers concerning famous crimes which they had worked on. The newsletters were wonderful sources of detective tales, colorful characters from the HPD history, and other tidbits of language and personality that added to my own mystery writing efforts.

Usually I would call Agnes with questions concerning the history of the HPD. However, this time she was telephoning me to ask if I was still collecting ghost stories. Of course, I assured her, I was always interested in firsthand accounts of the supernatural. Did she have a story for me?

"I can't tell you the story, Glen," she explained. "The police files on this case are still sealed. However, it was reported in the *Honolulu Star-Bulletin*. The officers involved in the case are still alive, but both of them refused to tell me anything about it. All they would say is that they had been blessed and they were told never to talk about what they had seen."

She gave me the date and page number of the issue of the Star-Bulletin in which the so-called "incident" was reported. A few days later I was sitting at Hamilton Library at the University of Hawai'i, running through the role of microfilm for 1942. Just as she described, the story was prominently featured on page 3. It was simply titled, "A Kaimuki Ghost Invades Home."

The details of the supernatural invasion as described in the newspaper were sparse. Evidently, the reporter for the *Star-Bulletin* who had summarized the police report was a skeptic who viewed the officers as "bull liars," drunks or insane. The article was dripping with ridicule and occasional humorous asides at the expense of the officers. Yet within the story was an incredible tale of terror that seemed lifted right from the script of a Hollywood horror film.

According to the few facts as written, two HPD officers arrived at a Kaimuki home at 11:30 one summer evening. As they got out of their cars, they saw an hysterical woman waving a *ti* leaf in both hands and sprinkling salt, screaming at the top of her lungs that her children were being killed. When the officers tried to calm her down, asking who was killing her children, the woman answered that it was her mother-in-law. When asked what type of weapon was she using, the woman answered that she didn't know.

"She died two years ago. She said she'd get revenge on me. Now she's killing my children."

When the officers went up to the porch to see what was actually taking place, they saw the woman's children levitating in the parlor, being thrown about, pinched and slapped by an invisible force. Trying to enter the house, both officers evidently were blocked by the same force that was terrorizing the children. Unable to enter the home, they watched helplessly as the three children suffered this supernatural assault, until it suddenly ceased at 1:30 AM. For nearly two hours, the officers had watched helplessly as this unseen supernatural entity had assaulted the family.

Immediately, I called up Agnes Matsushita at the police department. Since the tone of the story was filled with humor, I thought perhaps this was a "Halloween" tale made up for the benefit of public amusement. Was this really a police report?

"Absolutely, Glen," she confirmed. "The officers won't even talk to me about it. I wanted to write it up for the newsletter. I've seen the report and it wasn't written as a joke. Not at all. What do you think?"

I wasn't certain what to think about the case. It certainly conformed to the more famous "Kaimuki Ghost" assault in the early 1970s which was published in the *Obake Files: Ghostly Encounters in Supernatural Hawai'i.* And the tale made an excellent background for Honolulu International Detective Agency operative Arthur McDougal to appear in "The *Kasha* of Kaimuki," which was originally published in the Hawai'i Herald and then reprinted in *Obake: Ghost Stories of Hawai'i.* Unfortunately, a house located in Kaimuki was erroneously identified by a local radio station in 1996 as being the actual house in the *"Kasha"* tale! The occupant of the home was unfairly subjected to dozens of "ghosthunters," who night after night for several weeks gathered in the yard of the home, some even shouting at 3:00 AM "Obake come out!" This was NOT the house in the tale!

The exact location of the house in a district as large as Kaimuki, in fact, is not at all important. What is essential to understand isn't where these events took place, but why! And most importantly, if this could happen on one night 50 years ago in one house, couldn't it happen in your home, tomorrow night?

And had the unholy force indeed been caused by the mother-in-law as claimed by the hysterical woman in the yard? I've always had a difficult time believing that any mother-in-law, no matter what her anger at her daughter-in-law, would be capable of terrorizing her own grandchildren. Increasingly we have become aware of child abuse as a very real social problem within our Island community. Shocking tales of adult brutality unfortunately have become too commonplace. But if the spirit had such a hatred for the mother of the children, why didn't it attack the source of her hatred? Why take it out on innocent children, and not attack her sister-in-law?

In the tale "The *Kasha* of Kaimuki," I linked the incident to a Japanese folk myth concerning an unseen evil force that is conjured up through sorcery to tear apart the bodies of victims. The *kasha* makes a gruesome opponent for Detective McDougal, but the connection is entirely fictional. I know of no such Japanese-style paranormal being which has ever visited the Hawaiian Islands.

So the puzzle of what happened in Kaimuki remained unsolved, as more stories of other houses came to my attention where accounts of manifestations of a similar nature took place. *The Secret Obake Casebook* became filled with short tales of various individuals, all of them living in what they described as Kaimuki, who had experienced haunted moments similar to that of the incident reported by the HPD. These houses were located throughout the district, from Diamond Head to Kahala, from Kahala to the intersection of King Street, Wai'alae Avenue and Kapi'olani Boulevard, where Kaimuki ends.

In the summer of 1994 I was invited by Ruth Tang to investigate one such house located in a typical Kaimuki neighborhood. Unlike the "haunted house" of imagination, nothing about the exterior of this home would suggest that it was plagued by supernatural manifestations. Yet, the story that Ruth told was just as chilling as any tale of fiction—in fact, it may have been even more terrifying, because it was, after all, absolutely true. Since the house was so extraordinarily ordinary, without any of the menacing personality of the Amityville horror, it made Ruth Tang's testimony even more unsettling.

The three-bedroom, single-story house built in the 1920s was situated in the middle of a quiet avenue on a gentle slope with a wonderful view of Diamond Head and Waikiki. The home was first inherited by Ruth's father in 1960, when his bachelor Chinese uncle had passed away. The uncle had purchased the lot and house in the boom days of realty development, when areas like Kaimuki and Bingham Tract were prime properties for a small, but growing, class of Chinese and Japanese entrepreneurs settling in urban Honolulu. In those days, Kaimuki was popularly called the "Bronx of Honolulu," having its own mayor, Japanese gardens, a shooting range and, for a brief time, a zoo. Having no family, but becoming wealthy from a thriving market in Chinatown, the uncle purchased two house sites in Kaimuki. He lived in one home and rented the other. When he passed away in 1960, he left Ruth's father the property that he had for many years rented out to a variety of families.

Ruth and her husband first lived in the house in 1961, only a few months after they were married. Although the house being a rental unit had not been as well-kept over the years as they would have liked, the rent was, after all, free. As far as Ruth knew, nothing unusual or criminal had even taken place in the house since her great-uncle had first acquired it. The house and yard seemed very cheerful and, in accordance with her personal spiritual beliefs, the grounds had been blessed by an Episcopalian priest before she and her husband moved in.

Ruth recalled that the first year of her marriage was blissful, as the newlyweds worked hard to build up a nest egg in preparation for the birth of their first daughter, Cheryl Ann, in the spring of 1962. They set aside one of the bedrooms as a nursery, decorating it with cartoon wallpaper and hanging a colorful mobile from the ceiling above their baby's crib. Who would have ever thought that such a happy room, at such a special moment in the passage of one's life, would turn to terror?

It began ordinarily enough when Cheryl Ann was only three months old. She began waking up in the middle of the night, screaming her little head off. When her parents rushed into her nursery, they found her almost gagging in her crib, her little body feverish and trembling. Above her, the mobile which was attached to the ceiling was spinning wildly as if caught in a powerful gust of wind.

The parents at first thought that she had soiled her diapers or was hungry. But their baby continued to cry hysterically, even after they changed her diaper. Cheryl Ann refused her bottle so she wasn't hungry. Something else was disturbing their little infant as Ruth coddled her in her arms, trying to put her at ease. At first the mother hadn't noticed the rash that had formed about her daughter's neck. But on closer inspection she realized that Cheryl Ann must have been suffering from this very nasty skin inflammation that formed a reddish finger-like pattern upon her otherwise unblemished skin.

The doctor examined the baby the next morning, but the inflammation by then had greatly subsided. Skin rashes are not uncommon in infants, he reassured Ruth, after prescribing a lotion. It may have been her little shirt riding up on her neck while she slept that had caused the irritation. At any rate, since it had gone away and did not seem to be dangerous, the doctor declared Cheryl Ann to be in perfect health.

Two nights later, Ruth was again brought out of sleep by Cheryl Ann's screaming. Again, her infant was hysterical in the crib, the mobile spinning wildly above her and the inflamed finger-like rash burning on her child's neck. Cheryl Ann cried through the night as Ruth held her baby close to her breasts, protectively shielding her from all those thousands of childhood dangers that parents in their worse nightmares conjure up. The next day the doctor again tried to convince Ruth that her child, except for this skin irritation which always faded in the morning, was in excellent health. Perhaps Cheryl Ann was allergic to the detergent that Ruth had been using to wash her infant's pajamas. That afternoon all of the bedding and clothes of her baby were washed using a very mild soap. Cheryl Ann slept peacefully that night and every night after for two weeks. The rash had finally vanished.

When the screaming returned one morning at 3:00 AM, Ruth dashed to her baby's nursery anticipating that she would once again find her child agitated by the rash upon her neck. Only this time, she stopped and frozen at the door to the room, her body momentarily paralyzed in abject fear. The cries of Cheryl Ann were drowned suddenly in a hideous scream that shattered the quiet of their Kaimuki home. The scream, she realized, was coming uncontrollably from her own mouth.

Inside the dark nursery, illuminated only by a motorized merry-go-round lamp that cast out dancing shadows of horses leaping up and down upon the walls, Ruth watched, horrified, as the mobile above Cheryl Ann spun wildly out of control. An eerie wind like a tiny twister hovered above the colorful toy, which was lifting like the blades of an ascending helicopter. The wheels attached to the legs of the crib were rolling back and forth in little circles about six inches in diameter as the bars of the crib rattled furiously. For a brief, unbelievable moment, Ruth watched as the wheels then rose off the floor and Cheryl Ann's crib levitated about one foot into the air. The dancing horse shadows pranced devilishly on the walls, as a desperate mother broke her paralysis just long enough to snatch her infant out of the hellish crib that without its caged victim, crashed back to the floor.

One incident was entirely enough, Ruth explained to me, for the family to move out of that house immediately. She tried to explain to her father what had happened, but, although he was sympathetic, he found her account of the levitation outlandish. Hadn't she been sleeping? he reminded her. Perhaps she dreamt or hallucinated the crib floating in the nursery. There were no other witnesses to this manifestation except Cheryl Ann, who was far too young to tell anyone what had happened.

Ruth never doubted the supernatural truth of the horrible vision she had witnessed in that house. Her father simply put it on the rental market and began a long succession of short-term tenants over the next 20 years. No one seemed to stay in the house very long, Ruth noted. Local people born and raised in the Islands especially hated the house. Even if they had signed a two year lease, some of them would purposely violate the rules just to break their agreement. Her father never fully explained to Ruth what the complaints had been, perhaps fearful it would exacerbate his daughter's own alleged experience many years before. No one who rents property wants their real estate to have a reputation of being haunted.

When her father passed away in 1985, Ruth then inherited the nightmare house that she had long dreaded. Going through her father's personal papers after his death, she discovered that some of the former tenants had tried to convince her father that the house had been haunted. There were several letters of complaint that he had hidden in his files which confirmed what she had long known. Something in that house assaulted human beings.

Most of the letters were vague about the problem, saying that the occupants felt "uneasy" in the house. One complained about shadows in the shape of a human being that moved on the wall. Another said that her children had been slapped by an invisible force. The majority of notes simply said the house seemed to contain something "unnerving," "dark," "destructive," "unhappy" or "evil."

The most detailed letter came from an occupant in 1982 who stayed in the house only one month. He wrote an angry letter claiming that the haunting of this house should be disclosed to future tenants. He and his family, including his elderly mother, had moved into the home with no prior experiences with ghosts, poltergeists or any other supernatural being. In the first week of their occupancy, both he and his wife were "touched" by something in the house. Their children were terrified to stay in their room at night, saying that they also were "touched and pinched" by an unseen being. The last straw which convinced them to move was the night that the family was sitting about the dining room table enjoying their evening meal. The man looked across the table and, at his mother's throat, he clearly saw a large, dark hand appear, not attached to an arm or any other appendage. This hand grabbed his mother's throat just as she gagged on a piece of meat and nearly choked to death. No one else, including his mother, saw the disembodied hand. However, he was convinced that the materialization of the hand and his mother's choking incident were connected.

After reading all of these letters from former occupants, Ruth was convinced that the house had to be sold. For over one year the house was left empty until a buyer could be found—she didn't want to be responsible for any tenant's safety, whether they believed in ghosts or not. The disclosure that the house may be haunted that she included in the real estate description may have been a factor in discouraging anyone from buying the property, but she felt it was only right to be honest about the situation.

When the house was deserted for a year—the first time no one had lived in it since her father had inherited the place—the neighbors on one side called Ruth now and then with various little complaints. Why don't you turn off the electricity to the house? they would ask. Some nights the whole house would be blazing in lights that cast bright glares into the rooms of the neighbors. The electricity hook up to the house, however, was turned off when these incidents were alleged to have taken place!

The neighbors complained on another occasion about the grandfather clock in the unoccupied house. Why didn't Ruth either remove or turn off that bothersome clock? Some nights the neighbors would wake up to the chimes of a clock in the house that could be heard even next door. The repeated bonging of that old clock at 1:00 AM would seem to go on forever. The old grandfather clock that the neighbors heard, Ruth explained to me, belonged to her great-uncle. He had put it in the house in the 1930s basically just to store it somewhere. The clock was there in 1961, when she briefly occupied the house, and was finally removed by her father in 1982, when one of the tenants alleged that their children had accidentally smashed his baseball bat into the front cabinet glass. The clock was repaired and now was being kept at her father's house. Yet, the neighbors claimed to hear it chiming in the deserted home.

A "For Sale" sign was prominently displayed in the front yard the day that Ruth and I walked about the grounds of the house that had plagued her for so long. She had decided to let some tenants move in on a one year lease until she could get the house sold. Since they weren't local people, Ruth rationalized, they wouldn't have any trouble. For some reason, Ruth explained, only people born and raised in Hawai'i had problems inside that house. Mainland *haole* lived there without complaint. I privately thought that this was the first time I had ever heard about supernatural beings that make a distinction between "local" and *haole*—wondering also whether in this situation "for local only" was a blessing or a curse.

"Have you ever tried to bless the house again," I asked her, "after the first blessing when you moved in?"

"Many times," Ruth answered. "But they never must have worked."

"Did you ever bring in an Hawaiian kahu to bless the property?"

"Once, but he said he couldn't bless it."

"Why not?"

"He said it wasn't Hawaiian spirits causing the problem. When I asked him what race they were, that I'd go get a priest from that ethnic group, he smiled and answered that it wasn't human. It was an evil in the earth, under our house, that was here before human settlement."

An evil in the earth that was here before human settlement? This was the first time I had ever heard of such a thing—although it wouldn't be the last. I wondered if this explanation for the haunting of an otherwise friendly looking home in Kaimuki, which was unable to be sold, could be connected to a similar force that levitated children in another home 50 years earlier, and the famous "Kaimuki Ghost" that, as described in the *Obake Files,* materialized as a gruesome, disembodied hand in the parking lot of the old Oasis Nightclub, which once stood at the intersection of King Street and Wai'alae Avenue. All three tales shared so many supernatural elements in common, now all of them possibly explained by an old Hawaiian priest who told a woman that her property had an "evil before human settlement" situated in the soil.

Ancient legends are not only a marvelous form of entertainment, cultural awareness and mythical enlightenment, but, for someone actively trying to unravel our neighborhoods' on-going mysteries, also a source of wisdom. Legends, we are sometimes cautioned, should not be taken too seriously, especially when they involve supernatural beings. Myths have symbolic and historical meanings that transcend the actual reality of the heroes, demi-gods or ʻeʻepa, miraculous creatures.

Yet, one must stop and ponder the relevancy of a legend when it sheds light on the concept of "an evil before human settlement." One such legend was recently published in a valuable collection entitled *Ancient Oʻahu: Stories from Fornander & Thrum.* Based upon nineteenth century folklore collections of Abraham Fornander and Thomas Thrum, one of the stories concerns "Hanaaumoe," described as a "mischievous spirit" who once lived on the island of Oʻahu before human settlement. When the first human beings visited this island, Hanaaumoe would tempt them to shore and then, with other evil spirits, devour them. Hanaaumoe and his cohorts ate human flesh.

In an introduction to the story, Dennis Kawaharada writes that before human settlement, "Oʻahu was swarming with hundreds of thousands of cannibal spirits called akua." Before human beings could inhabit the Islands, these malicious beings needed to be subdued. The mythic hero Kaneʻopa was responsible for subduing these cannibal spirits on Oʻahu, while the restless ghosts of Lanaʻi were destroyed by that island's famed trickster hero, Kaululaʻau. And yet, while these human heroes destroyed nearly all the evil spirits on each island, there would always be one who escaped. On Oʻahu, Hanaaumoe somehow evaded the clever trap set up by Kaneʻopa and thus was never destroyed.

Murder marked other episodes in the criminal history of ancient Kaimuki. Kaumana was a demi-god who, in the days of the great chief Kakuhihewa during the late sixteenth century, lived in the area which today is called St. Louis Heights. He had come from Lahaina on the island of Maui with his parents, wife, several sons and 50 followers, arriving at Maunalua on Oʻahu, a valley now commonly known as Hawaiʻi Kai. There, this band of *malihini* began to steal food that had been grown by the people of that valley. When Kaumana became bored with this thievery, he visited the island of Kauaʻi. There, he met a *kahuna* or priest who told him that, if he would sacrifice his beloved, youngest son, "the road home would be shortened."

Greedy to fulfill this promised prophecy, Kaumana decided to sacrifice his youngest, most beloved son. To prepare for the ritual, he traveled about the island of O'ahu, gathering up all the items he needed to accompany the sacrifice. He visited Wai'anae, where he obtained a black hog, red kumu or goatfish, and a white cock. At Kahala he caught more fresh kumu; at Niu he obtained coconuts; and at Kuli'ou'ou he gathered the makaloa reeds to weave a *makaloa* mat.

Kaumana then returned to Maunalua and approached a pond that was situated in front of his home. Seeing his father in the distance, the youngest son eagerly swam through the water of the pond to greet him. When the boy reached the edge of the water, Kaumana drew up his youngest son, tied him with ropes and threw him back into the pond, along with all the offerings that he had collected. When the boy finally drowned, the sacrifice was complete.

Although he had committed this infanticide for the gain promised by the *kahuna,* Kaumana was grief-stricken by what he had done to his favorite child. With great lament and shame, he went to his wife and sons to confess his crime. That night a strong wind blew, the ocean became rough and violent and in the morning Kaumana's fishpond had disappeared. In its place was an expansive stretch of beach which made a fine path to walk upon. Thus the prophecy of the *kahuna* had been fulfilled. Instead of having to walk around the pond to approach his house, Kaumana's "road home" was "shortened."

Kaumana now raged in bitterness, his mind sunk in regret and madness for what he had done to his son. Finally, his deep, angry guilt turned to murder. One day he suddenly killed his wife and all of his sons. Then he began murdering all of the people with whom he had journeyed from Lahaina, until only four servants remained. With these servants, Kaumana went to live on the ridge between Palolo and Manoa valleys. In time his unabated torment darkened the skies above O'ahu and the four servants turned into powerful rains that sent torrents of floods through Kaimuki and Kapahulu and into Waikiki.

The floods and continued downpour broke through the walls of the great fishponds of Waikiki owned by the powerful chief Kakuhihewa. The taro farms and homes of the people were being destroyed. Informed by his *kahuna* that these rains were the result of Kaumana's murderous guilt, Kakuhihewa was persuaded to offer the demi-god a black pig. As the offering was being placed before the enraged murderer, Kaumana realized that this was a sign that he was going to be momentarily killed. To escape his fate, he quickly turned himself into a large stone.

When this story was recorded by Theodore Kelsey in 1919 for the Hawaiian newspaper *Kuokoa,* the informant, Solomon Kauai, was able to identify the exact rock containing the spirit of Kaumana. The location was identified at "Wai'alae Road where it meets Kapahulu Road running to Waikiki." This is the exact spot where the Oasis Nightclub used to be located!

In European countries, where ghostly traditions of murderous deeds reaching back hundreds of years are told in gothic haunted castles, it is not difficult to imagine the killing souls confined to the ancient walls of those eerie abodes. That the specter of a murderer would haunt the corridors and rooms where those gruesome acts took place seems wholly reasonable if not required by a sense of justice.

Perhaps it is more difficult to imagine that as beautiful a place as Kaimuki may be haunted by a centuries-old supernatural being that has no benefit of castle or crenelated tower to reenact its crimes. This unseen presence, whether it be an evil force of cannibal spirits older than human settlement or the murderous Kaumana, must find its purgatory in the land itself, the land which it once turned red with blood. Who is to say what the consequence may be of building our homes upon the grounds it once tread?

Of course, these are legends, the readers must keep telling themselves—legends that a storyteller has tried to weave into the modern occurrences of the supernatural. There is no academic, spiritual or supernatural justification to draw a direct link between these ancient stories and the power that levitates innocent victims, assaults terrified adults, or briefly materializes as a threatening, choking hand. As you convince yourself that these are only stories, imagine for just one moment that stalking even now through your peaceful neighborhood is an invisible shadow fueled by an aged appetite for things most foul, a shadow that even now may be rising behind you on your wall.

The telephone call from Debra Gallegos came many days after I had visited with her and her husband at their Waialua home. She was very apologetic for the rudeness of John, who had cut me off when I had asked whether any manifestations had taken place in their home. In fact, they had been disturbed by certain cold spots at the bedroom window just inside where the body had been found by Ikaika. Inexplicably, the area right near the window was especially frigid even on nights when the air was warm and humid.

She also let me know that Ikaika had stopped digging up holes in the yard and cane field. I remembered her giant dog and privately grimaced on my side of the phone.

"So life is back to normal?" I asked cheerily.

"Oh, yes," Debra answered. "And Dr. Grant?"

"Yes?"

"How's your life now?"

I didn't know exactly what Debra meant. Had I indicated to her that I had any problems?

"What do you mean?"

"John made me give the badge away to you. I didn't really want to, because I thought it was so cool having something like that from a murder mystery. But he claimed that at night he would hear it tapping on the desk where I had kept it. The badge would rattle about, as if it were actually alive! I didn't know what he was talking about. I never saw it move. Anyway, I hope you enjoy it."

I placed down the telephone receiver and looked across my office at the badge that was pinned to the wall. I look at it more often than I like to now, especially on those late nights when I'm working alone on my ghost story projects. Maybe it is my imagination, but on a few nights it has seemed that maybe the points of the badge have moved just a tiny bit, as I wonder—who was the unidentified corpse with the crushed bones and the bullet hole through the skull?

Dark File II:

When Ghosts Are Called and Hell Responds

The attic of Henry Wadsworth Longfellow's home in Cambridge, Massachusetts, was filled that afternoon in the summer of 1980 with artifacts, boxes, furniture and other historic items which once had belonged to America's honored poet laureate. Frank Butta, one of the historic interpreters at the home, had obtained permission from the curator of the Longfellow National Historic Site to show me "A Spiritual Letter" that had been found in a box of miscellaneous personal items from the Longfellow collection. All the artifacts in the attic were being kept in storage and generally were not for public display.

I had learned about the "spiritual letter" from Mr. Butta a few days earlier, when I had taken a house tour of the Longfellow home, located on historic Brattle Street, not far from Harvard College in Cambridge town. During my research for my dissertation in American Studies at the University of Hawai'i on "Summerland: Nineteenth Century American Popular Beliefs Concerning the Life After Death," I had traveled to Boston to examine archival materials on Spiritualism in the Boston Public Library. Since Henry Wadsworth Longfellow had been interested for a brief time in the popular nineteenth century fad of "rapping," "seances" and the "spiritual telegraph" to the otherworld, I was curious as to whether or not his historic home site had any materials reflecting this ethereal interest. This being the first time in my life to visit Cambridge, a house tour seemed obligatory.

My guide was a wonderfully friendly and enthusiastic gentleman who at first defied my stereotypic image of an "historic house guide." Frank Butta looked like a rounder version of Paul Sorvino, the "boss" in the film *Goodfellas,* and spoke with the same northend Boston, Italian-American accent made famous throughout the nation with the popular "godfather" films of the 1970s. When he introduced himself to the small tour group, he pronounced his name exactly like the word "Buddha," a similarity he made reference to when he padded his round stomach in comparison to the "happy Buddha" figure that is often seen at Chinese restaurants as a symbol of good fortune. While in my mind I unfairly redressed Mr. Butta in a double-breasted, three-piece suit with white spats and a menacing fedora, the information he conveyed as we toured the home was brought to life with his obvious love for history, Longfellow and this simple, elegant home in the heart of the intellectual capital of the United States. When he poignantly read those famous verses from "The Children's Hour" in the very room where they had been inspired, I could easily imagine bounding down the "broad hall stair,"

Grave Alice, and laughing Allegra,
And Edith with golden hair.

After the tour was over, I asked Mr. Butta if there were any artifacts or documents that the historic house site owned that were connected to Longfellow's interest in Spiritualism. Although he would always deny his association with the popular nineteenth century effort to make direct communication with the spirits of the dead, the popular author of "The Village Blacksmith," "Evangeline" and "The Song of Hiawatha" did once write that, as regards the existence of ghosts, "I hope it is all true, as a vindication of the Spiritual elements, now so submerged by the materialistic elements of our day."

For a period of time Longfellow had attended seances and other "trance medium" sessions at the urging of his brother-in-law, Thomas Gold Appleton. In 1861, Longfellow's beloved wife, Fanny Appleton Longfellow, was killed when her crinoline dress erupted in flames as she was wrapping presents near the family hearth. A single spark from the fire had ignited her dress, and Longfellow suffered severe burns on his face and hands when he tried to extinguish the horrible fire. Fanny's brother, Thomas, was so grief-stricken at the loss of his sister, he sought solace in Spiritualism. Having become an ardent believer in the truth of the "spirit telegraph," he attempted to bring Longfellow into the spirit circle by inviting famous mediums to the Cambridge home. Although the poet witnessed seances conducted by such famed mediums as Kate Fox and Cora Hatch, he concluded that "I was not much edified" by spirit communications.

Frank Butta smiled broadly and informed me that he was aware of Longfellow's interest in ghosts, but he knew very little about any Spiritualist connection. However, he recalled that in the attic there was a box which contained a few items that the curator had told him had to do with seances. He promised to ask the curator for permission to show me the box and gave me a telephone number to call in a few days for the answer. One week later, I was joining Mr. Butta in this special moment in the Longfellow attic, anxious to see and touch these few hidden artifacts that reflected one soul's quest to reach beyond the grave, to know for certain whether the spirits of our loved ones survived their death.

Necromancy is the term used to describe this ancient, often forbidden ritual of raising spirits. Practiced in one form or another by almost every culture in the history of the human species, the effort to communicate with the spirit world stems from the struggle of the heart to deny that death is final. If the rotting human corpse is our final, collective fate as living organisms, then what is the point of enduring all the little tribulations of existence, including aging, illness, sickness, heartache and pain? Why not merely hasten the end?

The hope in a life after death defeats our terror when contemplating the material decomposition of the body. This mortal coil, we can convince ourselves, is merely a shell—our loved ones have survived their passing from this inert matter which they have cast aside, no longer having need for the flesh. Organized religion is in part a system of thought that allows the believer to have faith in the spiritual survival of human personality so that we can concentrate on more mundane concerns such as going to work, caring for our families and paying taxes. However, when theology fails to provide this faith in an afterlife, especially during periods of intense grieving or spiritual doubt, some of us are tempted to seek out our own tangible and physical evidence that the spirits of our dead retain their personality in the great mystery to come.

Folk religion around the world is therefore filled with beliefs concerning the power of shamans or priests who employ magical techniques to directly communicate with spirits. In Hawai'i, nearly every ethnic group has a strong tradition of how such revered individuals can be utilized to reassure the living that their ancestors remain actively involved in their lives. Native Hawaiians of ancient times called the power to raise the dead *kilokilo 'uhane,* a secret ritual performed by the *kahuna kilokilo,* a priest who specialized in studying the stars for omens. Among the Japanese, such folk shamans are known as *odaisan,* who perform rituals of healing, exorcism and spirit-seeing. A large population of female Korean shamans are frequently sought out by a wide spectrum of persons in that society to contact spirits of the other world for the purposes of seeking advice and determining the future. The Chinese, Filipino, Portuguese, Puerto Rican, Vietnamese and Okinawan cultures each have their special seers who utilize a variety of necromantic rituals.

In the Judeo-Christian traditions, calling back the spirits of the dead is expressly forbidden. "If they have Moses and the Prophets," wrote American Protestant minister William Thayer in 1855 in an attack on mediumistic activities, "neither will they be persuaded though one rose from the dead." Faith in the basic religious tenets of Judaism or Christianity, in other words, is the only hope for eternal life—not fraternizing with ghosts. When King Saul hired the Witch of Endor to bring back the ghost of Samuel from beyond the grave, he openly defied these Biblical prohibitions against such "black arts." The threat of talking directly with the dead was such a concern of the Catholic and Protestant Church, which sought a monopoly on spiritual matters, that an extensive genocide was practiced against shamans or witches through the seventeenth century. Indeed, the infamous witchcraft hysteria in Salem, Massachusetts, in 1692 was first ignited when the West Indian slave Tituba taught the young women of the village necromantic rituals so that they could receive from the undead information on their future husbands.

As the theological cords of Christianity loosened on the grip of the human imagination in the nineteenth century, many men and women, especially in the United States, became fascinated with the possibility of using science as necromancy. If the telegraph could shorten communication between living persons on the earth, couldn't a similar "wireless" method be invented to connect the living with the dead? The first scientific evidence that the spirits of the dead could communicate with the living was the famous "Rochester rappings," when the Fox sisters in 1848 brought the ghost of a dead man into their Hydesville, New York, home who magically "rapped" answers to simple yes-and-no questions. The national excitement at the news of these rappings led, by 1860, to upwards of 10 million Americans claiming to have regular conversations with the spirits of their dead loved ones through parlor "sittings" or "seances."

Machines were even developed to scientifically prove that this "celestial telegraph" system was genuine. Professor Robert Hare, a distinguished chemist at the University of Pennsylvania, stunned the academic world in 1855, when he announced not only that he was a Spiritualist who regularly chatted with his deceased wife and Benjamin Franklin (who gave him an updated theory on electricity), but that he had devised a Spiritscope that would prove the validity of spirit communication. The complex device (pictured below) resulted in this renowned American scientist being howled down by the American Scientific Association and branded an "infidel" and a "fool" by the press.

Professor Hare's Spiritscope

The Spiritscope was, of course, far too cumbersome and impractical for home use. Consequently, an American toy making company in 1868 marketed a handy device known as a "planchette" ("little board"), which was sold throughout the country in bookstores. Invented in 1853 by a Frenchman named M. Planchette, this thin, heart-shaped wooden platform about the size of the human hand was held up by three legs, two on small wheels and the third a pencil with the point down. Participants in a seance would place their fingers upon the planchette, which would then move across a piece of paper to write messages or draw pictures under the influence of the spirits of the otherworld. In some cases, the messages were written, proponents of Spiritualism argued, in the exact handwriting of the deceased!

In 1890 the popular "planchette" was replaced by a newer, easier device to contact the dead, the "Ouija" board—a simple, painted plank with the words "yes" and "no" in the upper corners and the letters of the alphabet and numbers displayed in several neat rows. The practitioners of Ouija placed their fingers upon a small planchette, which would glide over the board spelling out responses to the questions of the living. There is some disagreement on who was the inventor of this "game," which has fascinated generations of American youth and "spirit-seekers." Some sources credit an American toy maker named Elija J. Bond as the inventor of the board. Other sources cite a Chestertown, Maryland, cabinet and coffin maker named E.C. Reiche as its creator. Reiche is alleged to have named the board "Ouija" on the advice of spirits that told him that was the Egyptian word for "good luck." The fact that the word "Ouija" is not in the Egyptian language did not seem to bother this coffin maker with a love for the mystical.

Whoever its inventor, the financial wizard who made the board a national craze was William Fuld, who founded the Ouija Novelty Company and went on to sell millions of the strange "talking board." A huckster of the first order, Fuld created the myth that the board's name was a combination of the French and German words for "yes." He also promoted his first edition of the board with the promise that "Ouija knows all the answers. Weird and mysterious. Surpasses, in its unique results, mind reading, clairvoyance and second sight."

In February 1927, after a slump in sales of what was sometimes called the "witchboard," Fuld climbed to the roof of a three-story building in Baltimore and allegedly "fell" to his death. Close associates were convinced that he committed suicide. Eventually Parker Brothers, the producers of the popular game "Monopoly," acquired the trademark and patent to the Ouija in 1966 which they still produce and sell throughout the United States in toy stores.

How and why does the Ouija board work? To some degree, as anyone who has played with the device will attest, there is sometimes a conscious interference in the progress of the planchette across the board by a player who wants to make certain that the "correct" answers are given! When the planchette moves freely and dramatically to the various letters, numbers or "yes" and "no" responses, some have theorized that this is a collective "psychic energy" of the various players that channels into the board.

This is the same "psychic energy" which is utilized when performing levitation parlor games. One such game involves sitting someone in a chair in a pitch-dark room with their eyes focused on a single candle. Four people stand, one each at the four corners of the chair, while the seated person begins to repeatedly think, "I am as light as a feather, I am as light as a feather." After a few minutes of absolute silence, one of the four assistants standing about the chair puts a single hand on the head of the seated person, with the other three one by one placing their hands upon the next. Finally, with four hands resting on the seated person's head, the top hand presses firmly down for about 30 seconds. The person in the chair feels his body sinking firmly into the chair. Then, very quickly, one of the four assistants puts one finger under the seated person's left elbow, another assistant under the right elbow, another under the right leg at the knee and the last under the left leg at the knee. Together they lift and, if all goes well, the seated person, no matter how physically large, will feel as if they are weightless, drifting up to the ceiling as high as the four assistants can reach. In effect, the body will be levitated! Having once been lifted several feet in the air by four young women who could never have done this feat under ordinary circumstances, I can attest to the strange feeling of shock and fear that the subject of the levitation feels as it is happening!

Is this the same "psychic energy" that is used by individuals during a crisis when a slim woman or even a child is able to lift the back of an automobile off of a person trapped underneath? Does this unseen force somehow move into the Ouija board so as to reveal subconscious answers from the deeper psyche of the people who are touching the planchette?

Or is this game, designed for "entertainment," actually reaching into the spirit realm, genuinely calling the ghosts of the dead who respond by foretelling the future, giving details of their past lives or information on how they died? Or is this "toy," as many believe, a deceiving gimmick placed into the hands of unsuspecting innocents who unwittingly become the minions of a dark and sinister power that feeds upon ignorance, gullibility and the curiosity of fools? When you have the audacity to believe that you have the mental power to boldly call out to the dead, have you the wisdom to know whether it is the dead truly responding? Or, as the files in *The Secret Obake Casebook* suggest, have you just sent a page to the bowels of Hell from which will come the seducing power of unfathomable evil and unmitigated guile?

The Sobbing Spirit on Punahou Street
Casebook Entry #244

Date of Entry:
March 12, 1978

Supernatural Category:
Restless Spirit/Ouija Board/Sexual Possession

"Have you ever used a Ouija board, Glen?"

The question came from one of the students in Dr. Dennis M. Ogawa's "Japanese American Experience" class at the University of Hawai'i at Manoa for which I was a teaching assistant in 1977. I had already gained a reputation for studying Hawai'i's supernatural, and Denise Endo's question seemed rational enough. If I was exploring the world of Island obake, I must have certainly tried to make direct communication with the spirit world.

"No," I lied. "I've never actually used that thing. Why?"

Once, as a teenager, I had played with a Ouija board owned by one of my sister Pamela's friends. Although she was two years younger than I, my sister was always able to get me to do things that down deep I knew would somehow get me eventually into trouble. Whether it be one early morning moving all of my parents' bedroom furniture onto the front lawn, selling tickets to the neighborhood children to see them sleeping in bed, or squishing bananas on the kitchen floor to ease the artful, ancient childhood skill of linoleum holua sledding, Pamela was always filled with devilish schemes that usually terminated with my being spanked.

The scheme she devised in October 1960, I must admit, was ingenious. One of my uncles who lived in Texas had just passed away that morning, and in the evening my father had driven my mother to the airport so that she could fly to Dallas for the funeral. My sister and I were home alone, so she called her girlfriend over to the house. She specifically requested that this girlfriend bring her Ouija board. Being, as a teenager, already an aficionado of ghost stories, I thought that her plan was both exciting, as well as a little frightening, for a 13-year-old who adamantly believed in ghosts, yet had never actually seen one. We were going to contact our deceased Uncle Leslie, Pamela decided, who had just crossed over to the other side. If anyone could come back, we reasoned, it would be a freshly arrived spirit.

We lit candles, asked a few questions of my uncle and yelled at each other, accusing one another of having purposely moved the planchette. The whole episode was ridiculous and disappointing. The only messages we definitely received were the ones that my sister forced on us by brazenly pushing the device to "YES" whenever I asked if my uncle was in the room. The experiment was a complete failure.

Later than evening, just before my father returned from the airport, I went into my brightly lit bedroom to do my homework. There, outside the window, I thought I saw our next door neighbor Bill Spiedel standing, staring into the room. Although the window was closed behind a screen, I could see his eyeglasses glimmering in the outside driveway lights. Since Bill and Dorothy Spiedel would sometimes baby-sit us when my parents were out, I naturally assumed he had come by just to see if we were all right. I walked right up to the glass and looked out into the driveway to tell Bill that we were just fine. Only it wasn't Bill at the window.

Standing in our driveway, looking in on me was my beloved Uncle Leslie, whom we had just tried to contact with the Ouija board. In life he had been a very obese man who had the kindest, most wonderful heart. A bachelor his entire life, my sister, brother and I were his only children and he adored us, always showering gifts on us when we visited his little country town of Bowie, Texas. A gentle smile was upon his rotund face, set off by the familiar wire glasses that were perched on his nose. He was wearing a nicely pressed suit and I could see attached to his vest a watch fob, which shined in the driveway's reflected light. A burst of tears broke as my childish, fearful heart couldn't understand how precious this moment could have been if I had only tried to talk to this man whom I so loved. Instead, I fled hysterically from the window, turning my back on a gentle spirit who had simply returned briefly to say good-bye. I told my father later that night what I had seen, and, though he comforted me that these mysteries are not to be feared, I always retained a dread of that window in my bedroom. I also vowed never again to touch a Ouija board, a promise I almost kept until I heard Denise Endo's story.

Denise had become concerned about her roommate, who had recently become very attached to playing with the Ouija board as a way to make contact with the spirit of a young woman who visited their apartment unit in a four-story building on Punahou Street in the Makiki district of Honolulu. Denise had moved into the one-bedroom apartment at the beginning of the school year the previous September. Having been born and raised on the island of Kaua'i when that island could still boast that it had only one traffic signal located in the middle of a sugar cane field, this was her first time away from home. She shared the apartment with a friend who had also grown up on the island of Kaua'i.

According to Denise, within a few weeks of moving into the apartment, both she and her roommate began to hear the cry of a woman in a corner of their bedroom. The first time that she had heard the sound, she assumed that the sobbing from the wall was coming from the next-door unit. Evidently someone in the room on the other side of the wall was very upset. A young professional couple who lived in that apartment must have been arguing or something, since the wife was quite upset. Both Denise and her roommate could hardly get any sleep—the sobbing coming from the wall was so loud.

A few nights later they both again woke up in the early morning to hear the woman next door sobbing loudly. Maybe this was a sound the couple made during lovemaking, they joked. Taking a glass from the kitchen, they turned its open end against the wall to see if they could amplify what in the world was going on next door. Was the husband abusing her or simply a wonderful lover? During the day, these people seemed like a nice, upright Chinese-American couple who were very much in love with each other. Maybe at night, Denise thought, their personalities radically changed.

The wall was comprised of concrete cinder blocks which were evidently too thick to allow them to hear any of the argument next door. But the sobbing was very audible coming from the corner. As they listened, they realized that this was not someone crying from pleasure or love. The woman was either deeply sad or in very desperate pain.

The sobbing sounds continued intermittently until finally, building up her nerve, Denise decided to ask the neighbor very discreetly whether or not she was all right. One afternoon they were both in the basement laundry room waiting for the dryers to finish their cycle when, woman-to-woman, Denise tactfully inquired how everything was going in her life. With that simple question, she had hoped that the woman would open up. Instead she only smiled, shrugged in a way to indicate life was going on normally, and said "okay."

Realizing that she wasn't going to confess any abuse going on with her husband, Denise finally asked very matter-of-factly whether she had been feeling well or not.

"My roommate and I are a little concerned because, well, we sometimes hear you crying. Have you not been well?"

"What do you mean, crying? I'm perfectly fine."

"Oh," Denise answered a bit surprised, "we thought we heard you crying in your apartment."

The woman almost seemed a little insulted that Denise would suspect something would be wrong with her. She reassured Denise that she was in perfect health and that if Denise had heard sobbing in her apartment, it certainly wasn't her crying. Of course, Denise realized, she could just be covering up her husband's abuse.

One month later, the next door couple left for a two week vacation to the mainland. Their apartment was empty. The lights had been off for days and the doors were locked and secured. Yet, one night Denise and her roommate were again awakened briefly by the sounds of a female crying in the wall at the corner of the room. That was the night they both realized these sad sobs originated not in this world, but from a ghostly source.

In the last month, Denise then informed me, her roommate and the roommate's boyfriend had taken up the Ouija board to find out the history of the sobbing in the corner of the room. At first Denise joined in as if it were a game, but one night when asked "who is the spirit who cries in our apartment," the board spelled out "A-L-I-C-E." In time her roommate was starting to act a little obsessive about the spirit of "Alice," who had begun to move the planchette about the board every night, spelling out all kinds of messages about her life on the earthly plane. In fact, the reason Denise mentioned her current "haunting" to me was that she felt that she almost had acquired a new roommate—that "Alice" had become the third tenant in the apartment.

"It is so bizarre, the way my roommate is acting," she finally said. "I've heard that the Ouija board can be dangerous. Do you think you'd be interested in coming over tonight to check it out? She and her boyfriend will be home tonight about 9 o'clock and I know they'll play with the board. They do it every night now."

At 9:00 PM that evening I was cruising Makiki neighborhoods looking for an impossible parking place and arrived 30 minutes late at our "seance" with the so-called "witchboard." Denise introduced me to her roommate, a stunning Filipino-Hawaiian-Chinese woman by the name of Chantelle Ching, who earned money as a model and Waikiki "roaming" photographer. With her boyfriend Chris Wong, who was obviously a body builder with an immaculate set of pectoral muscles that showed through his flesh-tight shirt, she had started a little independent photography business. Chantelle would visit an exclusive nightclub or restaurant in Waikiki, such as Valentino's, Canlis or Bobbie McGee Conglomeration, and take photographs of romantic couples sitting at their table. She'd drop the roll of film off at Chris' nearby office, where he would develop the pictures just in time to return them to the couple before they left the restaurant.

Chantelle's eye-catching appeal no doubt enticed more than one gentleman to pay for her services, just for a chance to have five minutes of conversation with her. The Kaua'i beauty had an unblemished, milky-brown permanent tan that was accentuated by her compelling black eyes. Her shoulder-length golden-brown hair matched her skin color and was fashionably cut with a full body that was poplar in the "disco '70s." Standing a tall five feet six inches, she held her full figure with a posture that signaled to any man who looked (and what man didn't) that this was a woman who was confident of her seductive charms. I was almost embarrassed to look at her, afraid I would obviously stare, as I greeted her with a silly smile.

"You're late," she snapped back at me with a little frown. "We were supposed to contact her at 9 o'clock. Alice will be upset."

Chantelle turned and went back into the bedroom, quickly followed by Chris and Denise. It seemed apparent that, although Chris himself was a handsome, professional model, he doted over every whim of Chantelle's. And Denise may have also felt a little intimidated that her best friend, who was so spectacular looking, seemed to want to be in total control of the household. I obediently followed the trio into the bedroom, where the Ouija board was sitting on a small Japanese-style folding table located in the corner of the bedroom. They had placed large wax candles all over the various tables, drawers and bed stands in the room, giving the room a warm and attractive glow more suitable to romance than ghost-seeking.

"Everyone put your finger on the board and shut your eyes," Chantelle directed. "You will see, Gary, that this really works. We have really made contact with the spirit of Alice."

"Glen. My name is Glen."

"Oh, sorry." Some impression I had made.

In a few minutes we were all listening to Chantelle ask Alice out loud if she were in the room. We waited a few minutes as the planchette floated around the board, not certain of which direction it wanted to go. Suddenly, it flew to "YES."

"Okay. She's here," Chantelle said. "Aloha, Alice. This is your

Chantelle. Are you here?" Again the planchette flew to "YES."

"May I ask Alice some questions," I said, looking over at Denise. I couldn't at that moment say for certain that Chantelle was fully in control of that planchette, but I was hoping Denise would catch my eye signal to be more assertive. She and Chris barely touched the planchette, which allowed Chantelle to move it without restriction.

"All right, but they all should be answered by "yes" or "no."

I agreed to frame my questions simply and, for the first time in my life, spoke directly to a ghost of a sobbing woman through a Ouija board.

"We already know a lot about her," Chris volunteered. "Chantelle has been doing this every night for a couple of weeks. We can tell you what you need to know."

"I'm interested in what the spirit has to say," I told him. I wasn't interested in hearing their version of events—I wanted to get it straight from the ghost.

"Your name is Alice?"

The device flew to "YES."

"You died in this room?"

"NO."

"You died somewhere else?"

"NO."

"So you died in this room?"

"NO."

I was stumped already in the first four questions. How could she answer "no" to all those questions?

"Did you die in this place?" Chantelle then rephrased my question.

"YES."

"This building is only 20 years old, Gary," Chantelle explained using my new name. "She died here before the apartment was built."

"Okay, I get it," I said confidently. I would need to be more careful with my questions and cross-examination.

"You died here a long time ago?"

"YES."

"Can you tell us the year?"

"She only answers 'yes' and 'no,'" Chantelle angrily corrected me. "I told you that when we started."

Suddenly the planchette flew to the number "9." It stayed there a second and then slid over to "8" and stopped.

"1898?"

"YES."

Now we had a date, I thought, smiling at Chantelle, who had been mildly put into place by Alice. She could communicate beyond "yes" and "no." Maybe the spirit even liked me a little bit, I thought pleasingly.

"Did you die violently?"

"NO."

"Did you die in an accident?"

"NO."

"Did you commit suicide?"

The planchette didn't move for a few minutes. Maybe the spirit didn't want to think about her suicide. Maybe it was a horrible tragedy she was trying to forget. Suddenly the planchette flew to "NO."

"You died peacefully?"

"NO."

"You were murdered."

"NO."

I was getting very impatient with Alice because she wouldn't give me a straight answer. Chantelle saw my frustration and asked, "Did you die of a broken heart?"

"YES."

"Did your husband die? Were you a widow?"

"NO."

"Did your husband desert you?"

"NO."

"Did your husband cheat on you?"

The planchette now spun crazily on the board. Everyone's finger seemed to be guiding it in this direction and then the next, as if we were trying to each give a different response. This went on until, finally, the planchette flew out of our grasp, as it popped off the board and hit the wall.

"Stop trying to move the planchette, Denise," Chantelle said accusingly.

"That wasn't me," Denise protested. "I'm not trying to move it. Why would I do that? I think this is scary."

We brought the planchette back to the board and, with our fingers repositioned, I again asked if Alice's husband had cheated on her. This time the device was motionless.

"She doesn't like answering that question," Chantelle finally said. "We've tried to get an answer to that, but she never can respond. I think her husband must have cheated on her."

"Was your husband a bad man?"

"YES."

"Did he hit you?"

"YES."

"Why have you come back to this room?" I asked, switching to open-ended questions. The "yes" and "no" ones were getting boring. Chantelle gave me a quick, nasty stink eye. However, even she was surprised when the planchette moved to the letter "C" and then floated about the board before again stopping at the letter "C."

"You came here to see Chantelle?"

"YES."

"Why? What do you want of her?"

The planchette moved to the letter "F."

"You want her to do you a favor?"

"NO."

"You want to be my friend, Alice?"

"YES."

"Why?"

There was no response from the planchette.

"Why do you need Alice to be your friend?"

Again, the planchette seemed dead. Alice was not giving us any further answers that night.

Chantelle chided me for trying to ask open-ended questions, but I reminded her that we had found out some important information through those questions—that the spirit had purposefully returned to this sphere for the friendship of Chantelle.

"I already knew that," she then said, with a slight air of arrogance. "Why do you think I have to be touching the board for the spirit to talk? It won't work without me."

I bet it doesn't work without you touching the board, I thought to myself. It seemed to me that Chantelle was the one who knew all the answers and guided the planchette for the purposes of convincing the rest of us that "Alice" was real. I was certain that she had been doing all this consciously, but she was too pleased with herself to not be getting psychological satisfaction from her new dearly departed friend.

Later that evening I had a cup of coffee with Denise at Coco's on Kapi'olani Boulevard. She confessed that she thought that Chantelle was overreacting to the Ouija board and possibly even making all of it up. However, she assured me, she hadn't been making up the sounds of the sobbing in the corner of the room. Those they had both heard and it was a genuine sound. I suggested that the woman next door may not have been fully candid concerning her own domestic situation—why should she have confessed to being abused? Or it could have been their lovemaking.

"We haven't heard it since we made contact with Alice," Denise then explained. "The sobbing has stopped. Are you saying they stopped having sex next door?"

"That's interesting," I said. "The crying stopped when Alice started talking through the board?"

"We haven't heard it since."

I then pressed Denise to share some of Chantelle's background. Since they had grown up together on Kaua'i, I was certain they knew every detail about each other. Chantelle's father had deserted her mother, Denise told me, just after she had been born. He moved to another island and never paid any child custody. Chantelle's mother, who was from the Philippines, carried the burden for the entire family, which included four children, by working at two jobs—a custodian for the county of Kaua'i and a housekeeper for a hotel at Po'ipu.

When Chantelle was in high school, she had a boyfriend who was very insecure about her maturing good looks. At the age of 16, she began to do some modeling for hotel brochures and that angered her boyfriend, who on a few occasions hit her. She wasn't badly beaten, but one night he slapped her around enough to call the police for protection. One of the reasons she decided to move to O'ahu with Denise was to get away from the abusive boyfriend.

The pattern seemed now to be making sense. The spirit of an abused, heart-broken woman feels simpatico with a beautiful, young, living woman who has suffered the same type of abusiveness. The fact that Chantelle herself feels warm and friendly to the ghost is a reflection of her own needs, I reasoned, to be close to someone who has suffered abandonment and violence perpetrated by men. The seance, I now fully understood, was indeed a therapeutic encounter for the living who evoked disembodied memories of past unresolved feelings into a setting by which anxieties and neuroses could be faced. My "pop psychology" seemed convincing enough as an explanation for these weird events on Punahou Street.

Later in the week I did a quick research into the background of Punahou Street. In the time period during which "Alice" died in 1898, there were many exclusive mansions on the broad, tree-lined street between Beretania Street and Wilder Avenue. On the Waikiki side of the street lived such distinguished families as the Dillinghams, Whitneys and Spreckels. On the 'Ewa side of the street lived the Widemanns, Frears, Beckers, Alexanders and Dowsetts. This was a moneyed-class of Honolulu's elite society that ruled the Islands with iron fists behind kid gloves, and who knew how to keep their indiscretions very well buried. I never was able to determine any family whose residence had been at the precise site of Denise's apartment building—this land had been reserved for a dairy farm. But on this property in the 1890s there had been smaller cottages used by caretakers and other employees who often came and went with the course of business. Perhaps a couple had lived in one of those cottages, a couple whose violent relationship was kept a dark secret from their upper-class neighbors.

When the school term was over, Denise and I lost connection for a few weeks until the spring term of 1978 commenced. I saw her as she was registering for classes in the madness of Klum Gym.

"Hey, how's your sobbing ghost?" I asked. She didn't smile at my little joke, but went on to tell me that she was ready to move if Chantelle didn't stop all that nonsense with the Ouija board. It was like she was a changed person. Every night, instead of going out with her friends or Chris, she'd come home from work and sit with that witchboard into the early morning. She no longer bothered to include Denise or Chris in the ritual, preferring to move the planchette herself. Alice and Chantelle had become such good friends, they had little time for anyone else. The ghost was now giving full messages using the letters of the alphabet, spelling out long paragraphs of thoughts or advice for Chantelle. In turn, the beautiful young woman was even confiding her private, intimate thoughts to Alice.

"It is so weird, Glen," Denise confided. "I've moved into the living room so she can have the room alone. I won't go in there. You can hear Chantelle laughing some nights as if the two of them are telling each other private little jokes. And some of those jokes, well, they seem to be dirty, if you know what I mean."

Denise was too embarrassed to explain what was going on in the bedroom, but it seemed that Ouija had become the psychological mirror for all of Chantelle's deeper frustrations. The first-stage sympathy that she had felt for the abused, lonely spirit was turning into dementia. It didn't seem healthy at all to be talking to yourself, using the presence of "ghosts" as an excuse.

I wasn't certain how I could help without the intervention of a psychiatrist, but Denise reminded me that Chantelle still respected me as an "authority" on parapsychology. Perhaps if I talked to her about the spirit, I could convince her to let the entity go to the otherworld. It was never safe fraternizing on a daily basis with unhappy ghosts.

Chantelle was not pleased when Denise, Chris and I suggested that we all talk to Alice together that evening. She told us that Alice doesn't like talking to anyone else except her now. I convinced Chantelle that my purposes were simply scientific, that I wanted to gather proof on the existence of spirits. Maybe "Alice" could tell us about the afterlife, the nature of Heaven, the existence of Hell, or other information on what happens to us when we die. "Alice" could become Hawai'i's own "Seth," an entity on the mainland that inspired several national best-selling books on the nature of the afterlife.

"Alice isn't interested in anything like that," Chantelle protested. "She's only interested in my life and my well-being. She says that she is my guardian spirit."

"Well, let me ask her about guardian spirits, then," I continued to argue. "She wouldn't mind telling us about that, now would she?"

Finally the oracle board was set up, the lights lowered and candles lit as our fingers touched the planchette. In a few minutes the wooden platform began to move about the board with such ease that we hardly needed to put our fingers on the device. There were no jerking, hesitating motions so common to the Ouija, no circular motions waiting for someone to pull the planchette this way or that. This device was moving as if an unseen force indeed inspired it.

After confirming "Alice's" presence, I thought it would be useful to gather more information on the ghost's background. Could she tell us her last name? There was no response. What was your address on Punahou Street? No response.

"Did you know your neighbors?"

"YES."

"Can you spell their names?"

The planchette didn't move.

"What was your husband's surname?"

"Alice never talks about her husband, Gary," Chantelle suddenly said, taking her finger off the board. "You don't have to answer that, Alice."

"If the spirit can't give us its surname, Chantelle, then maybe it isn't a ghost at all. Maybe it is only a psychological phenomena. I've done a little historical research into this area and I can't find any information that your Alice has really verified. If she can give me a name of a neighbor or her husband's name in 1898, then maybe I can believe her. Otherwise, maybe we aren't dealing here with a spirit at all."

Chantelle's eyes seethed in a private rage at me for even suggesting her best new friend wasn't what she claimed to be. Even more determined now to prove to me that the spirit was real, she started to put her hand back on the planchette. We were all returning to the Ouija, when suddenly the planchette moved slightly with no fingers touching it!

"Did you see that!" Denise screamed, jumping away. "It moved!"

"It could have been the table moving," I reassured everyone. "I may have bumped it accidentally with my knee."

At that instant, a bright flash went off in the semi-darkened room, momentarily blinding me. Chris, the consummate photographer, had taken a photograph of the planchette with his camera just after Denise had screamed. No one saw the device move again, but the thought that "Alice" had herself touched the Ouija board for a brief moment occurred even to me. Could the concentrated force of the spirit's presence be so intense that the planchette could move without human fingers?

Chantelle was furious with everyone now for having doubted her Alice's existence. Can't we see that the spirit was real, that it had moved the planchette? We had angered Alice, she screamed. Ordering everyone out of her bedroom, she slammed the door behind us, as she locked herself in the room with her witchboard and "Alice." When Chris plaintively apologized at her door, Chantelle told him to do something with his body and camera that was anatomically impossible. The dejected young man excused himself, apologized for Chantelle, and then said goodnight. He had work to do in his darkroom. This was definitely not a relationship which had much of a future.

The next morning I received a call from a frantic Denise that she would like to meet me at Chris' tiny Waikiki photo studio located on Lewer's Street, just behind the old Gump's building. When I arrived, Chris and a few friends were busy carrying a lot of photographic equipment out of his office. I noticed that one of the items was a very scorched enlarger that looked like it had recently been in a fire. Then I noticed that a few more of his friends threw huge pieces of carpet into a trash bin. The carpet was blackened and burned.

"I had a fire last night in my darkroom," Chris said quietly. "It was bizarre, Glen."

"I'm terrified now," Denise added. "I can't go back to my apartment, not after what happened here last night."

I still didn't know what had happened, except that there had been a fire in the darkroom that had burned the carpet and destroyed the enlarger. The landlord was furious at Chris and was threatening eviction. The damage to the walls, ceiling and carpet wasn't too extensive, but would cost a few thousand dollars that Chris didn't have. Plus, he had no insurance on his office or its contents.

That evening after he left the aborted seance, he had returned to his office to complete some work. It was after midnight when he decided to develop the roll of film that he had taken that day, including the photograph of the Ouija board. After developing and hanging the negatives to dry, he was getting the enlarger ready to make a print of the photo when the darkroom light, which glowed red in the room, began to swing back and forth on the cord it hung from, above his head. The enlarger then began to slightly rattle while the walls of the darkroom also shook. It felt as if the building were vibrating from a very low rumbling, possibly an earthquake. Fearful that he would be trapped in the room, he went to the door to rush out of the building. However, when he tried to open the door, it wouldn't budge! It seemed that the door was caught or jammed on the frame. Throwing his shoulder full force against the door was to no avail. There was no exit through that door.

The rumbling continued when behind him he heard a small pop, like a firecracker. He turned to see that the red darkroom bulb had exploded, a tiny burst of flame from the light falling from the cord into several rolls of film hanging in the room to dry. The film flared up so surprisingly that Chris was momentarily stunned, as the broken bulb unbelievably spurted out more electrical sparks and tiny balls of fire ignited the carpet on the floor, a blackout drape over a window, and the wooden table upon which the enlarger had been mounted. In moments the tiny darkroom was filled with fumes and leaping flames as Chris finally reacted, grabbing a tiny fire extinguisher that he fortunately kept mounted on the wall. In a moment the fire was smothered in the life-saving white foam, as the sting from the smoke of the blaze burned his eyes. Now that the fire had been put out, he turned his attention to the door, which was frozen shut. Again, he tried to turn the door handle, but this time it opened without resistance. Even before he pushed the door open, it swung slowly by itself on its hinges, releasing into his inner office the horrid smelling fumes and smoke. His darkroom was destroyed, but at least he was safe.

To me these events sounded highly unusual, but not as preternatural as Denise and Chris claimed. He believed that something wanted to burn him to death that night, that an evil spirit had followed him to his office. The walls shaking, the door jamming and the light bulb bursting was just too much of a coincidence. There had been no earthquake on O'ahu that night, but Chris' office was in an old building with an ancient central air conditioning system that rattled terribly when it started up. The doorknob was not new and neither was the door, which Chris had "cockroached" from his parents' home when he first built the darkroom inside his office. Old doors poorly installed can freeze. As for the bulb exploding—unfortunately, such accidents do occasionally happen.

Despite my rational explanation, Denise was insistent that we do something to get Chantelle away from that Ouija board. My only remedy was to call a Hawaiian woman who had once been introduced to me as a "trance medium." This was a person who would allow the spirits of the dead to literally speak through them. I was sure that Chantelle would be excited by the prospect of actually being able to talk directly with her "Alice." Consequently, I called Sylvia Crabbe to tell her the entire story of Chantelle and her attached spirit. She agreed to look into the *pilikia* or trouble, as she described the situation.

As I suspected, Chantelle was very excited at the notion of meeting a trance medium who would be able to allow her to chat directly with her dead friend. A large space was cleared in the bedroom where the sobbing spirit had first been heard, and a table was set up with several chairs in a circle. Mrs. Crabbe, her husband, Denise, Chris, Chantelle and myself would be the only ones in attendance. Chantelle insisted that her Ouija board be placed in the middle of the table, claiming that "Alice" told her that she required the board always to be present even when a medium was being employed.

Mrs. Crabbe and her husband were slightly uncomfortable that evening as they crowded into the tiny bedroom on Punahou Street. The air was humid and, since the apartment had no air conditioning, the presence of so many of us in such a small space made it difficult for her to breath. She explained that she needed as much room as possible, since during her trances her body sometimes was affected by the possession.

Although she was a Native Hawaiian, Mrs. Crabbe's power and belief stemmed, she explained, from the Egyptians to whom her people were connected through transpacific migrations thousands of years ago. Her spirit guide was actually an ancient Native American shaman named Owanda, who had once lived in the Pacific Northwest. Mrs. Crabbe had extensively studied Theosophy and claimed to have integrated the wisdom of Eastern philosophy with the ancient kahuna rituals. She was an unusual lady.

When Mrs. Crabbe took one look at the Ouija board on the table, she ordered it out of her presence. Such devices, she said, were dangerous because they were often put in the hands of novices who knew nothing about the magical or spiritual powers with which they were tampering. It was compared to a child being given a loaded AK-47 with the safety clip off. Taking her place in the sacred circle, she finally went into a deep, sleep-like state for what seemed like 10 or 15 minutes. Several of us began to yawn, half-suspecting that this offbeat person had actually just nodded off instead of entering a trance.

Her great frame under the very large *mu'umu'u* gently rose and fell. I noticed that her face was very manly and fleshy, and a few long hairs extended from her chin. An explosion of frizzy salt-and-pepper hair about one foot in length went in all directions from her head. Her skin was very pale, suggesting that her Polynesian ancestry had been greatly mixed with the nationalities of Europe. When she began to snore, I had to pinch myself to keep from laughing.

The snore, however, soon softened to a sob which emanated from her throat as if in a hollow tube. This sobbing immediately frightened Denise, who looked knowingly at me. This must have been the sound which first lured these two women into the series of eerie events culminating with this seance. Chantelle was wide-eyed, with a broad smile that suggested she anticipated that someone she loved very much was finally returning home.

"Chantelle?" the medium finally spoke in a delicate female voice. "Chantelle, are you with me?"

"Yes!" the young woman answered, her eyes glassed and voice trembling. "Alice?"

"I am the one in life they called Alice," the voice in Mrs. Crabbe said. "I've suffered so much in this world. Oh, my dear, sweet friend, you have been so good to me. You are my darling friend."

"It is time for you to leave this earthly plane," Mr. Crabbe then said. He was a tall, thin *haole* man in his late sixties who, except for a quiet "hello" during introductions, had said nothing until now. During his wife's mediumship he always assisted her, protecting her body from impure spirits and always trying to "rescue" the spirits through direct communication. He now tried to coax "Alice" from the apartment on Punahou Street where her lonely existence had come to an end.

"I wish to stay with Chantelle," the spirit answered Mr. Crabbe. "I would be lonely without her."

At that moment another voice suddenly entered Mrs. Crabbe. This voice was deep, manly and filled the room with a quiet prayer in a language totally unrecognizable to any of us.

"This is Owanda," said Mr. Crabbe, "her spiritual guide."

Owanda finally spoke English, although it was difficult at first to understand his sentences since he spoke in a singsong fashion, with some words rising in pitch and then dropping strangely into a deep bass. Then he kept saying one word over and over, running its syllables up and down the musical scale. At first I couldn't understand, until finally it became very stunningly clear.

"Beware. Beware," were the words which Owanda repeated.

"Beware of what, Owanda?" Mr. Crabbe asked.

"Alice is not the spirit of a woman. It is a man."

A horrific scream at that moment came from Chantelle as she fell back on the floor, her back hurled across the floor to the corner of the room. The fall backwards knocked her unconscious, as her head snapped up against the wall. The shock sent spasms through her body as her head now jerked back and forth as though something were slapping her face. A deep groan emitted from her chest as her whole body trembled from shock.

"Don't touch the slut," a man's sinister voice different from Owanda's now growled through Mrs. Crabbe. "She's mine."

The room then filled with this demon's torrent of filthy words and horrible deeds which we were told would be inflicted upon Chantelle, her poor body shivering all the while on the floor. All of us who witnessed this scene had nearly fallen out of our chairs, as well—even Mr. Crabbe, an experienced hand at such trance seances, admitted later that he had never seen a spirit so demented as the one that seized his wife's larynx. Although Chantelle had probably fallen out of her chair in fear, striking her head against the wall as her body went into shock, I couldn't help but fear that this poor, beautiful woman was actually being molested on the floor by a foul deceiver who had invaded her home, won her confidence and then enjoyed her rape.

The incident ended as instantly as it had started. Chantelle suddenly calmed down as Chris wrapped her in a blanket and laid her out on the bed. Mr. Crabbe was in deep prayer, holding his wife's trembling hands as the profanity from her mouth ceased, followed by a laugh which I would never forget. The deep, mocking laughter was from an evil man who in life had molested and abused his wife, yet knew not one ounce of remorse. It was the soul of cruelty itself that was emanating from Hell.

Later that night, once she had recovered her composure, Mrs. Crabbe explained to us what had happened. Although she had no memory of the events which we had witnessed, she understood that Owanda had come forward to warn us that the spirit of the sobbing woman actually had been the husband who had driven his wife to an early grave after years of abuse, adultery and sadistic treatment. Her soul was safely embraced in the light of heaven, healing and awaiting incarnation, Mrs. Crabbe explained in theosophical terms. The husband had been cast into an eternal service to wickedness, a servitude the old sinner enjoyed.

When he felt the sexual presence of Chantelle in the apartment, he seduced her through her open hearted empathy for abused women. He used that camaraderie to get closer to her, the Ouija board as his portal into this world of flesh. Now that his true identity had been revealed, the gate to his demonic sphere had been permanently shut. At least for the time being.

The aftermath of these events were all tidy. The Ouija board was taken into the parking lot, placed inside a tin garbage can, dowsed with lighter fluid and ignited. Within an hour, the trash can was filled with ashes, which were then ceremonially buried in the yard of the apartment building. Chantelle and Denise moved immediately from the apartment, which was blessed by Mrs. Crabbe for the safety of future occupants. Chris and Chantelle were reunited and two years later were married at a ceremony at the Hilton Hawaiian Village to which I was invited under the name "Gary Grant."

About a month after our seance with Mrs. Crabbe, I was pretty convinced that the events described in this casebook were best explained as psychological turmoil within Chantelle over her earlier abandonment by her father and abuse by a former boyfriend. Mrs. Crabbe was aware fully of the history of the case before she ever visited the apartment. She may have been sensitive or even "psychic" to Chantelle's former history and subconsciously tied all of these strings together in a dramatic bow for a supernatural package. The voices of the sobbing spirit, Owanda and the evil husband did, after all, flow from her mind and body. The Ouija is a toy that becomes deadly not because of spirits and demons, but because of the psychological transferences by the living on that little object.

Then I received a small envelope from Chris Wong that contained a small note and photograph for my files. The note was very short and explanatory. The night of the fire, the photograph of the Ouija board had not been destroyed. Although part of the roll of film had burned, the frame with that picture was still intact. He produced a copy for me, which was attached to the note. At the bottom he scribbled, "P.S. Look at the Ouija with a magnifying glass. What do you think? Chris."

I held the photo up under one of those jeweler's eyeglasses that are used for examining diamonds. In the photograph, the Ouija board was on the low table, the planchette in the position where it had come to a rest after moving by itself. Denise and I are pictured in the photo with surprised looks on our faces, having just watched the device move supposedly under its own willpower. However, under close inspection, there is something in the photograph that is truly remarkable. On the planchette is a finger touching it—a large, manly finger. While at first glance I thought that it was actually my forefinger on the Ouija, my two hands are clearly away from the board. Denise's hands are also nowhere near the planchette. The finger is clearly visible touching the Ouija, but fades where it should be attached to a hand. Although I love collecting uncanny photographs, I burned this finger from Hell.

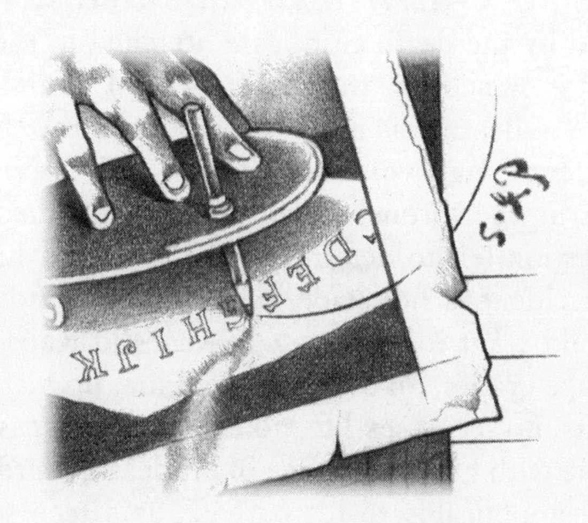

In Search of Erin Liu
Casebook Entry #1675

Date of Entry:
June 7, 1989

Supernatural Category:
Ouija Board/Haunted Condominium/Poltergeist

Erin Liu was dead. That was an established fact, verified by the death certificate attached to the Honolulu Police report, a certificate signed by the chief medical examiner at the Iwilei morgue. The cause of death was neatly typed out in the space provided: the deceased had suffered massive head injuries and internal hemorrhaging caused by a fall. Erin, the coroner reasoned, probably died instantly.

The only question left to determine was *why* Erin Liu was dead. Had the fall been an accident, a homicide, or a suicide? Finding no motive for why someone would want to murder a 16-year-old Roosevelt High School student with average grades, an average social life, no teenage gang connections, no bad habits, no secret sex life, no enemies, no signs of breaking-and-entering and no one with him at the time of his death, murder seemed unlikely. Suicide seemed implausible to his parents, as a teen self-inflicted death always seems to those closest to the deceased. "What could he have been despondent over?" "We gave him everything he wanted!" are the common responses to a police inquiry suggesting perhaps a child had taken his own life. Evidence to the contrary notwithstanding, Erin Liu's death did not seem like a suicide.

"Accidental" was the only plausible reason left for Erin's tragic death. The lanai of his 27th floor condominium was secured with a very strong railing, which was fully intact when the police investigated the place where he had fallen over. Had he been trying to climb along his lanai to maneuver his way to the next-door neighbor's condo, perhaps for the purposes of petty theft and then during the burglary lost his balance? Perhaps he was doing exercises on the lanai and tripped over the railing. While an accident was officially listed as the reason for his death, there were no witnesses inside or out of the condominium who could explain how the young man could have fallen.

So how did Erin Liu find himself falling over 270 feet down the side of his Nu'uanu high-rise home? As he fell, what nightmare vision did he see in the last horrifying split seconds of his life? What horrifying thoughts run through the head of a person plummeting through space, watching the pavement rush upwards to meet them? These questions concerning the death of Erin Liu were to remain unanswered. All that could be said for certain was that Erin Liu was dead.

Or was he?

My involvement in the death of Erin Liu in 1989 was wholly tangential through my association with Garrett Naughton. I had become casual friends with this instructor at Kapi'olani Community College who, a few years earlier, had participated as a humanities scholar in the Chicken Skin '85 Ghost Story Conference. Garrett's academic interest was Asian philosophy, but his personal religious beliefs included a firm rooting in occultism. When he wasn't contemplating the sound of one hand clapping, this otherwise intense young man was reading tarot cards or throwing I Ching sticks at Puck's Alley's "psychic faire," or spending his Saturday nights with a small group of students parked at Morgan's Corner, Acid Hill, the Chinese Cemeteries at Pauoa or Manoa valleys or at another Honolulu mortuary waiting for the statue of Jesus Christ to dance. He consumed fantasy comic books, science fiction and horror stories as if they nourished not only his night-sided mind, but his small, delicate frame made more wispy by the fact that he was one of the original vegetarians before the diet became fashionable.

In January 1989, Garrett called me with a fantastic story. A group of his students and himself, he claimed, had made direct contact with the spirit of a young man who had died in a tragic fall at the condominium where Garrett lived in Nu'uanu Valley. Utilizing a homemade Ouija board with an upside down whiskey shot glass as the "planchette," he and his students were having regular "talk story" sessions with the spirit. Did I want to participate in some of these extraordinary rituals of necromancy?

Remembering my earlier unhappy experiences with the "witchboard," I cautioned Garrett that such a toy could have dangerous consequences if the practitioners were not of strong mind.

"I'm an Asian philosophy major!" he reminded me. "Don't you think I know what I'm doing?"

"Garrett, everything you know is from a book," I admonished him.

"You and I are two peas in a pod. The only way we touch mysteries is on the printed page. You have no idea what spiritual things you may be tangling with."

"Glen, that's why you and I have to do this together, okay? Maybe we can both learn something."

I reluctantly agreed to meet with him for a few beers and review what had taken place thus far. That evening I was sitting in the back bar area of the Kaimuki Inn on Wai'alae Avenue quaffing a couple of brews and trying to listen to Garrett shouting over the *karaoke* singing in the background. He showed me his handwritten log of the events that had taken place thus far. They were scrawled in a black-and-white composition book that had been given the name "Ouija."

Evidently the sessions with the talking board had begun about two months before, when Garrett and a group of his students in an "Introduction to Religion" class met in one of the old army buildings still standing on the Kapi'olani Community College campus. Fort Ruger used to occupy the lands near Diamond Head which were eventually converted to a college campus. Before the new facilities were built, classes were held in some of the old barracks, administration buildings and officers' quarters that were part of the military base. The building where the first seance was held was numbered 933.

There were several K.C.C. students participating in the seance, including Ron Correira, Gary Young and Ford Hariguchi. They were all enrolled in Garrett's class and shared his fascination for comic books and ghosts. Their first session with the board was dated in Garrett's journal as November 8, 1988. The session started with simple questions such as, "Is there a spirit present?" The answers were innocuous and meaningless. They used the simple board and shot glass that Garrett had constructed.

On November 10 the four men repeated the session and, again, Ouija spelled out gibberish to all of the questions. However, when the question was raised about Garrett's future, the board finally responded with a very clear, but shocking, answer.

"You are the son of the Devil."

"Garrett is the son of the Devil?" one of the students asked.

"You are the son of the Devil," Ouija repeated. The session that evening finished very abruptly. Future use of the Ouija was postponed until the group again felt secure enough to inquire into the spirit realm.

The entry for December 5,1988 was interesting. "Ouija answers every question with the same response. 'E.L' will tell you. No one knows what

'E.L.' means. Is it a name of someone?"

On the next Saturday night Ron, Gary, Ford and Garrett again gathered in Building 933, in room 102 to consult the board on the identity of "E. L." The transcript of the questions and their responses were carefully recorded by Garrett in his journal:

Q. Where should we play Ouija?

A. Room 111.

[Margin note written by Garrett: "Before we began I had walked into 111. But walked right out again. The room 111 was too cold. We stay in room 102."]

Q. How many people are present at our seance?

A. 3.

[Margin note: "Incorrect response. There are 4 of us present."]

Q. Are we to experience anything unusual tonight?

A. Something will appear in 18 minutes.

Q. What will appear?

A. The Devil.

[Margin note: "Time: 1:20 AM"]

[Entry aside: "At 1:38 AM, almost to the second, the doorknob of room 102 started to turn very slowly. The clicking sound seemed to be amplified. Those present in the room looked at each other with a bewildered if not scared expression. When the door finally swung open, standing in the darkened hallway was the campus security guard! It seemed as if he was just as scared as we were. As he looked into the room he would see a chalk circle drawn on the floor, four people huddled within the circle, and a Ouija board on the table, a candelabra and other assorted candles. All of us, including the guard had a big laugh.

"Ron and Ford now inform us that when we first had approached building 933 at about midnight, they saw a red light in one of the windows of room 102. I said that no such light existed in the room. When we first entered the room, Ford said that he also saw a faint glow in the back of the room. This I believe was their imagination and nothing more.

"At about 2:00 AM we moved to room 111 as instructed by Ouija. The following questions were asked of the board."]

Q. You stated that the Devil would be here. We have not seen him. Where is he?

A. Go into the next office.

[Margin Notes: Garrett and Ron go into the next office, close the door, turn off the lights and wait for about five minutes. Nothing happens."]

Q. (Ron asking) I didn't see anyone in the next office except Garrett.

A. Who do you think that was?

These rambling notes and scrawled margin notes of this strange seance in Building 933 somewhat startled me. I wasn't aware that Garrett was so deeply involved in the methods of the occult that they would have put ritualistic chalk drawings on the floor, burn candelabras and other techniques of the magical arts. I almost wanted to ask him if he had dug up a corpse, wearing an article of its clothing and eating a piece of its flesh as is common among necromancers. The whole thing seemed a little ludicrous.

"So what does this mean when the Ouija said, 'Who do you think that was?' Are you the Devil, Garrett?"

He laughed nervously and reminded me that the board a few days earlier had said in reference to him that he was the "son of the Devil." This was perhaps why, when they asked how many people were present at the seance, the board answered only "3." Garrett wasn't counted as a person, but as a demon.

A subsequent journal entry showed that the seances continued throughout December. The board gave no significant responses except, in reference to Garrett, it again noted that he was still the "son of the Devil." On the last session held at Building 933, dated December 23, the board answered all inquiries with the same answer, over and over.

"E.L. will provide answers."

The journal ended there.

I told Garrett that, although this was all quite intriguing, I didn't think that there was anything going on with these incidents except the odd answers of the Ouija, which could be one of his students trying to scare him with answers like "son of the Devil." Maybe this was "the revenge of the philosophy students," I said laughingly.

"I don't think so," Garrett said quite seriously. "I found out who E.L. was!"

"Oh, who is E.L.?"

On January 9, 1988, just one week ago, Garrett was called at about 8:30 PM by one of the security guards at his Nu'uanu condominium. He informed Garrett that there had been an accident with his automobile. He had better come down to the parking lot. As he went to the elevator, he heard some of the residents who had just come up from the first floor all buzzing about some accident. Someone, he concluded, must have hit his automobile while it was parked in the lot. In the distance he began to hear a siren like an ambulance or police. This must have been a huge accident, he worried, as the elevator doors opened and he stepped into the lobby.

"Mr. Naughton, please come over here to my office," the chief of security said. "You don't want to go outside now."

"What happened to my car? What kind of accident was it?" The sirens were now wailing through the Nu'uanu night, pulling into the front of the condominium. Several people in the lobby were gawking at all of the confusion, while a few couples rushed their children in from the parking area.

"Your car was involved in a horrible accident."

"Someone hit my car? Was someone hurt?"

"Someone fell on your car, Mr. Naughton. We aren't certain who it was, but he landed right on your automobile."

"What?"

"I'm afraid your car is totally smashed."

One hour later the police allowed Garrett to examine his car, following their investigation of the area and removal of the body. One of the officers had tried to wash off the roof with a hose, but in his haste it had not been a complete job. Blood was splattered across the hood and trunk of the automobile. Pieces of the victim's skull and scalp were found on the dashboard, as his head crashed through the front windshield. His body had smashed into the roof, which now looked like a crushed accordion. The top of the car had been so violently hit, both side windows had shattered. The gaping hole in the middle of his windshield was edged with crimson blood, pieces of hair and a small portion of the deceased's ear. The car was demolished.

Garrett was still shaking when he went back into the building, trying to think of the protocol required by his insurance company following an accident. In all of the shock and confusion, he hadn't even thought of asking who the person was that had landed on his automobile or why they had jumped from the building. He went back to the office of the chief of security who was just finishing a telephone call with his supervisors.

"Excuse me, can I help you, Mr. Naughton?"

"I'm sorry, but who was the person who landed on my car?"

"It was one of the boys who lived on the 27th floor. The Liu family."

"What was his name?"

"Erin Liu."

"E.L. will provide the answers," Garrett thought, as he went to his 30th floor apartment, drank a glass of wine in the darkened living room to calm his nerves, and finally fell asleep on his couch as a Nu'uanu rain beat against his lanai window and a wind howled.

The next night Garrett had gathered his three spirit-seeking students in the parking lot, where his car was still waiting to be towed to a wrecking yard. He placed his Ouija board on the top of the car and asked that, if the dead spirit was present, to enter the board.

Garrett hadn't taken any notes that evening, but he related to me how the board immediately spelled out the message "Have a seance" to the question, "Is the spirit present?" When they asked why they should have a seance, the answer was "I want to speak to you."

"Who are you?"

"E-R-I-N" was spelled out by the board.

"That was just a few days ago, Glen," he said. "Now, what do you think? Is it worth investigating now?"

We left the Kaimuki Inn that evening, agreeing to rendezvous that weekend at his apartment, with his three students, so that I could witness his open "hot line" with the world of the dead.

When I arrived at Garrett's 30th-floor unit that Saturday evening, his living room was prepared for the ceremony to bring Erin Liu back from the dead with appropriate ritualistic symbols and candles. Although Garrett had struck me as a gentle soul who sought "Pureland" in his spiritual quests, his apartment was more decorated for satanic covens than enlightenment. A huge, cardboard placard with a hand-drawn pentagram and a lit candle at each point was placed in the middle of the living room floor.

I was introduced to Garrett's students who all formed a circle around the Ouija board, which was on the floor near the pentagram. Garrett directed the questioning of the spirit who quickly entered into the shot glass, sliding it to the various letters to spell out its messages. The spirit identified itself as "Erin."

As the letters of Erin's name was being spelled out, all of us heard a light, musical sound in Garrett's bedroom. An *'ukulele* that Garrett had left on his bed was gently strumming, as if someone or something was running its fingers over the strings. When we rushed to the room to see what was making the noise, the strange sound stopped. No one was in the bedroom.

Following this unsettling incident, I decided that I had had enough for the evening. The students agreed with me that calling back the dead may not be the appropriate thing to do in this case—especially since Erin had died such a violent death. None of us was psychic or spiritually prepared for this meddling with the veil of death. Garrett vigorously disagreed, urging us on with an unusual intensity. I had never seen Garrett as animated as he was that evening or as enthusiastic about any project. He persuaded his students to return the following night, while I told them that I would be unable to attend any further ceremonies.

Garrett kept in touch during the next few weeks, trying to persuade me to return to the circle. I told him that I didn't mind being kept abreast of his niele search for Erin Liu, but I definitely wouldn't participate in what I believed was an intrusion on the realm of the dead. Every few days he'd drop by my office and allow me to photocopy his journal entries. With only slight editing, these are the series of events with the Ouija as recorded by Garrett:

January 20: Ron C. was to come to my apartment after work at about 10:00 PM. Ford was to arrive later at about 11:30 PM. When Ford finally arrived, since he had just gotten off from work, he went to take a shower. I was talking to Ron and suddenly realized that he was not answering me. He seemed to be in a trance. His eyes were open, staring into space but it was as if he was asleep. I called him but he gave no answer. When Ford came out of the shower, I asked him to look at Ron. He also noticed the strange trance that Ron seemed to be in. Finally, I gave Ron a kick and he "woke up" rather startled. He asked what was the matter and I told him how he had been in a trance. He did not believe a word of it and felt that Ford and I were playing games with him. I started to feel very funny about the Ouija that night and canceled our plans.

January 21: The board was calling for a seance with Erin. Nothing significant happened this week.

January 26: We meet at again at my apartment after work. The seance included two new players, Russell and Karen, who are Gary's friends. After about an hour (about midnight) I got tired so I decided to lie down. Ron was sitting on the floor next to the couch. All of a sudden he said, "What's happening? I don't feel good. Something is happening!" Ron was then silent.

I went over and looked at him, and he was in the same trance condition that he was in the other night. His eyes were open and staring into space. I asked the others to come over and look at him. We called him and asked if he was all right. He started to mumble something which we couldn't make out. Gibberish. We shook him but he gave no response.

Suddenly he "woke up" and said—"what are you guys sitting around me for? What's wrong?"

We explained to him and he got angry. He says that we were calling him weird or some kind of freak. He was most upset that Karen, one of our new players, would think that he was strange. He screamed at us that he could never face her again. Ron stormed out of the apartment and the session was over.

January 28: Nothing happened during the seance. Ouija was silent. Ron was absent.

January 29: Ron agreed to return to the sessions. There were five of us including Russell, Ford, Gary and me. We questioned the board.

Q. Will anything happen tonight?

A. Yes.

Q. What?

A. E.L., E.L., E.L., E.L., E.L., E.L., E.L., E.L., E.L.

Q. When?

A. Soon.

Q. What is soon?

A. Five minutes.

We glanced at our watches. In exactly five minutes it would be midnight. The candle flame was flickering wildly. Ron stated that he was "feeling strange" again. This time I was prepared and asked that a circle be formed by joining hands. I was on Ron's left, Russell was on his right and Ford was directly across from him. As we joined hands, Ron suddenly fell back and started to talk.

Ron: I can hear him walking.

Garrett: Who?

Ron: Erin.

Garrett: How do you know?

Ron: He's coming here.

Garrett: Where is he now?

Ron: He's in this room and now he is standing behind Ford!

At this point Ron passed out. Russell felt a "cold spot" next to him. We tried to revive him by shaking his body and calling his name. No response. Suddenly he sat up and we asked him if he is all right.

Ron [Erin]: This is Erin.

Garrett: Why are you here?

Ron [Erin]: I did not want to die. I will not die. I'm here and I won't leave this body. Garrett, your car killed me. I'll be waiting for you. I will kill you. You killed me.

Ford: Garrett did not kill you.

Ron [Erin]: His car killed me.

Gary and Russell: Leave Ron's body! Leave Ron's body!

At this point there seemed to be a struggle between two spiritual forces within Ron. His spirit was trying to regain control of his body while Erin would not leave. Ron's body was shivering as the struggle continued.

Gary: Erin, you're dead. Leave Ron's body.

Ron [Erin]: If I must die, then we [Erin and Ron] will die. We will wait for Garrett and all of you.

Supposedly Erin was now getting angry and would take a life with him. So we took Russell's crucifix off and put it on Ron. Without breaking the circle, we joined hands as Ford went to his car to get a cross that he kept on his rearview mirror. Russell and Gary started to say the Lord's Prayer. For the first two or three times, nothing happened, since they were merely reciting words without adding any meaning. Some of the words of the prayer were incorrect. Then Ron started to speak again.

Ron [Erin]: No, no don't say that. You're killing me. You're sending me away. Don't please. I don't want to leave.

Russell and Gary were now repeating the Lord's Prayer over and over.

Garrett: Leave Erin. Leave Ron's body.

Ron took a deep breath, shut his eyes and was suddenly silent. Ford came back in a few minutes and we put another cross on Ron's chest and called to him. He gave no response. We shook him and called him again, urging his spirit to re-enter his body. He suddenly "woke up" and said, surprised, "Hey, what are you guys holding my hands for?"

After we explained, Ron got very upset and depressed. He couldn't conceive anything like this happening to him. Then he started babbling that "I don't believe it! I've always been good. I study hard, listen to my parents. You guys are lying to me and trying to make me nuts."

February 2: Ron was furious today at school. Accused me of trying to use him as a guinea pig, to experiment with him. He said that we were destroying him. I said that I didn't mean to hurt him. We had nothing to do with his trances. Whenever he is in our company, he is now extremely moody and depressed—silent and pensive. This is in direct contradiction to his usual nature.

February 3 through March 4: We "cooled" things off by not trying to get further involved with Erin. However, for me it has become too late. It is like getting on a roller coaster and then asking to get off right in the middle of the ride. We have decided, however, not to have Ron around because we feel it is best. It seems that in our presence he is susceptible to being "possessed."

March 6: We held an evening seance in Nu'uanu Valley in the woods off the Nu'uanu Pali Road. There is a very nice area accessible on a water reserve trail only 20 minutes from the road. We brought along mats, the pentagram, candles and Ouija. We had two new players: Linda and her mother, a European woman named Valerie. We first dedicated the board to Erin and then began the seance. The response was fantastic! Not only did Erin speak to us through the board, but Linda and Valerie played and communicated with several different spirits. They communicated with Veronica and Baba. Veronica is Valerie's dead sister who died when she was about three years old. Valerie doesn't remember her except that she is her sister. Baba is a young Samoan boy, only 10 years old, who told us he was an evil spirit who wanted to stay evil.

Suddenly Valerie began to tell us about our past lives. She said that I had lived nine lives and one life was as a bad priest. In my next life, Ron is to be my father, and Erin is to be my son. It was an extraordinary evening of spirit communication in the woods.

March 9: Tonight some friends came to my apartment for dinner. One of the instructors from K.C.C. named Barbara joined with her husband, Conrad. I also invited Russell and Ford. During dinner I asked Barbara if she ever saw the Ouija board in action. She was very curious so Ford, Russell and I showed her how it works. Conrad asked if he could also play. Within 10 seconds of touching the board, Conrad went into a trance. Playing with the board by himself, the shot glass swirled around the board with amazing ease. Conrad's eyes were closed, his head tilted backwards. The glass on the board was moving so rapidly that we were afraid that it would fall off the board. We asked questions and Conrad (through the board) answered. It was not Erin's spirit. The glass went over each letter precisely without misspelling. The board became possessed by other spirits who identified themselves as Satan and Baba. Satan stated that Erin was "lost" and had left the board.

Then Erin very briefly appeared in the board and stated that he was afraid and was "losing control." Other forces were pushing him out of the board. Ford and Russell took off their crosses and placed them under the shot glass. The glass stopped moving as the chains on the crosses, which were now under the glass, quivered like earthworms crawling over the board! I placed my finger lightly on the glass next to Conrad's finger when the glass jumped into the air. The two crosses slid across the board and flew onto the floor. Checking the crosses, we found that Ford's chain had become tangled and knotted.

Conrad slumped in his chair in a trance-like state, got up, then went into the bedroom to lie down. He was mumbling something incoherent, so I got a ti leaf, crunched Hawaiian salt on it, mixed the salt with some water, and wrapped it around a cross. We placed this bundle on Conrad's forehead. I also forced some salt into his mouth.

After an hour, Conrad walked out from the bedroom and did not believe anything we told him about what had happened. He said that he believed he had simply fallen asleep.

March 20: Since the night of Conrad's possession, strange occurrences are taking place away from the Ouija. Ron's bedroom door now opens regularly by itself. Several nights ago my blanket was pulled off of me within seconds after going to bed. Ford has heard knocking on his door. When he answers, no one is there.

Last night when I returned to my condominium, I was stopped by the chief of security.

"Can I tell you something?" he says to me. "Every time you walk into the building I feel something cold following you. It's strange because it doesn't happen with anyone else. This 'thing' seems to follow you into the elevator."

Ron, his mother and I have gone to a Chinese temple in Kalihi. I asked the temple priest for some advice. What could be following me?

"There is a spirit after you," he said "It is a young man whom you've never met, but who recently died."

If Erin is here, I trust him completely. I'm certain his attitude has changed since he first blamed me for his death. I want to educate him for his next life. After all, won't he one day be my son?

This was the last entry that Garrett Naughton showed me concerning his journal of a quest to use the Ouija to raise the dead. I would like to believe that Garrett's conclusion that Erin Liu found some kind of peace in the spirit realm is true. My friend was very eager about becoming the boy's father in some future life, since, when someone falls 27 floors and dies upon your car, aren't your fates intertwined?

I had these thoughts that May afternoon in 1989, only a month after I last saw Garrett, when I attended his funeral in Nu'uanu. He had jumped from his lanai on the 30th floor, falling to the pavement without striking any car. His mother, who flew over to the Islands from Oregon for the funeral, kept asking me why Garrett would do such a thing. The night before he committed suicide, he had called me with one simple message: "Glen, the spirit's out of control. I must leave this building." I told her that I thought that meant he was going to move. I had no idea he intended to take his own life—if indeed he had.

When I visited Garrett's apartment for the last time, I noticed that his mother was packing the Ouija board in a box to be given to the Salvation Army. I stopped her, took the evil little device and stood at the lanai overlooking Nu'uanu stream hundreds of feet below. I flung the talking board as far as I could and watched it fly like a boomerang into the breezy valley air, over the tombs of O'ahu cemetery, past the crypt of the Royal Mausoleum, above mysterious Kapena falls where it finally vanished into the twisted woods that concealed the stream below.

Garrett Naughton was dead. Or was he?

I wasn't about to find out.

The curator's box contained a few items which had once belonged to Longfellow, but defied cataloguing. The only two which interested me was a planchette and a neatly folded piece of yellowed paper labeled "A Spiritual Letter." The planchette was a simple, unadorned wooden platform with two legs attached to little wheels and the third a pencil. There was no history associated with the planchette—it may have actually belonged to his Spiritualist brother-in-law, Thomas Gold Appleton, but ended up in Longfellow's possession.

Frank Butta carefully opened up "A Spiritual Letter," but the writing was wholly unintelligible. I had no idea what it said. Then Mr. Butta explained to me that this was an example of automatic writing communicated by the spirits through the planchette which was backwards.

"Backwards?" I asked, puzzled.

"Backwards. You know, like Alice in Wonderland, *"Through the Looking Glass."* I smiled, thinking of this big, gruff fellow with the streetwise lingo reading Alice in Wonderland in his spare time. "You need to read it in a mirror."

The only mirror was in a small side bathroom used by the staff. We walked down from the attic and he let me take the letter inside the small room by myself—there wouldn't be room enough for both of us. I turned the light on and held the letter up so that I could read it "backwards."

Suddenly what had been unintelligible was transformed into a message from the spirit world to their "Friend," Mr. Longfellow. As I held the piece of paper in my hand I felt suddenly connected to another century and an American quest to know for certain whether there is a life after death, whether these bones can live again. An eerie feeling overwhelms the researcher at these unforgettable moments in their quest to touch the past. The little letter in my hand communicated all the vain, and sometimes silly, attempts we humans have made to verify the existence of ghosts by using the meager tools at our disposal instead of simple faith.

A copy of "A Spiritual Letter" today hangs framed on my Mo'ili'ili office wall. Like others, I've been tempted to call back the dead. If Thomas Edison had not died before he could perfect his "talking machine" that would link this world to the world of spirits, perhaps today we would be able to use our cellular phone to check in on our long-departed loved ones whom we miss so much. I have only one fear if such a device were truly available today—the fear that keeps me from dabbling with Ouija, planchette or any other form of necromancy. If I make that phone call, who in the hell is going to answer on the other side?

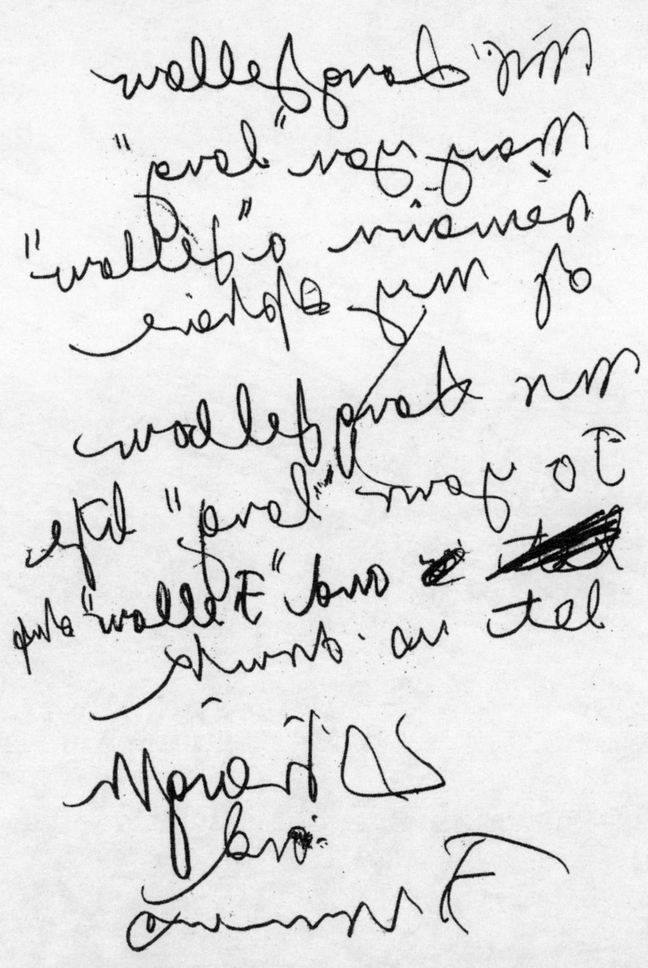

To read "A Spiritual Letter" hold this page before a mirror (Courtesy National Park Service, Longfellow National Historic Site)

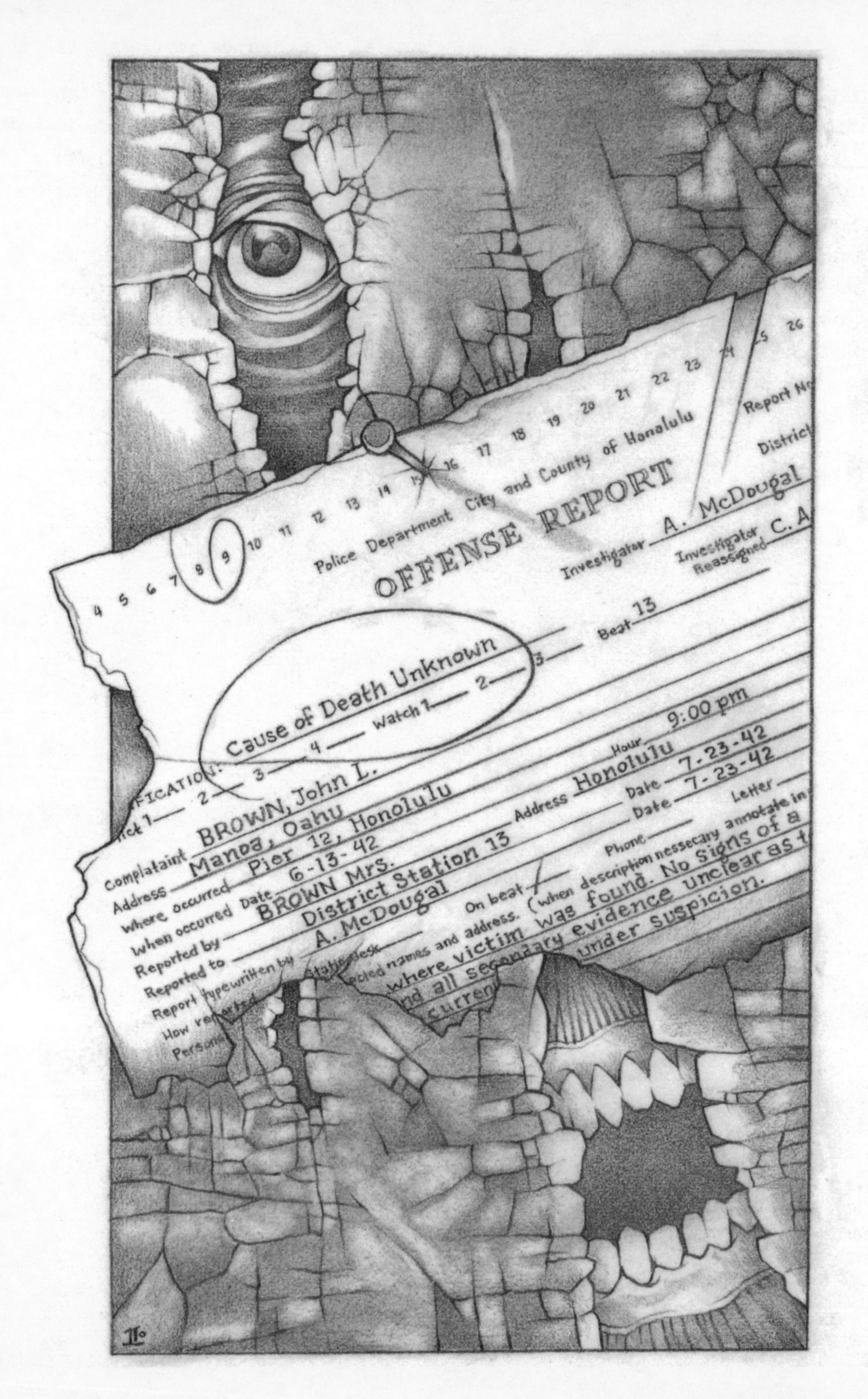
4 5 6 7 8 9 10 11 12 13 14 15 16 17 18 19 20 21 22 23 24 25 26
Police Department City and County of Honolulu
Report No
OFFENSE REPORT
District
Investigator A. McDougal
Investigator Reassigned C. A
Beat 13
Cause of Death Unknown
Watch 1 2 3
FICATION: 1 2 3 4
Complataint BROWN, John L.
Hour 9:00 pm
Address Manoa, Oahu
Address Honolulu
Where occurred Pier 12, Honolulu
Date 7-23-42
When occurred Date 6-13-42
Date 7-23-42
Reported by BROWN Mrs.
Phone
Letter
Reported to District Station 13
On beat
Report typewritten by A. McDougal
Station desk
names and address. (when description nessecary annotate in
where victim was found. No Signs of a
nd all secondary evidence unclear as t
under suspicion.
How reported
Person
curren

Dark File III:

When Death Lives in the Word

The emergency telephone call came from one of the Honolulu TimeWalks staff, who had me pulled out of one of my American Studies classes at Hawai'i Tokai International College on a matter of what she described as "life or death." Rarely have I been given this type of message right in the middle of a lecture, and a thousand thoughts of the darkest type rushed through my head. My stomach was churning as I called the TimeWalks number to find out who had died or what terrible calamity awaited. When the walking tour reservationist answered the phone, I could barely hear her, due to hysterical screaming in our offices. Through the incredibly high volume of the background noise, I finally could understand her trembling voice begging me to come back to the our Mo'ili'ili offices as fast as possible. In an obvious understatement, she explained to me that "someone was angry."

My class was over in 15 minutes, at 11:40 AM, at which time I rushed over to Honolulu TimeWalks to find the staff of the entire second floor of the building discussing what had been the "assault" on the office.

"Did you see that guy's eyes?" I heard one person saying. "I thought they were literally on fire!"

"I thought he was going to have a heart attack!" said another.

"I thought I was going to have a heart attack," said the reservationist who had called me earlier.

As they saw me entering the office, all of the staff greeted me with "stink eyes." If looks could kill, I would have been a dead man.

"So, where were you?" said the tour reservationist who had evidently received the bulk of the tirade by this mysterious angry person. "You are never here when something bizarre happens. You bring these things into this office, but you are never around to handle them when they explode."

I tried to calm everyone down to figure out what in the hell was going on, but their adrenaline was still pumping at 3,000 RPM. From what I could gather, a man had barged into the office, claiming angrily that I had stolen something from him. He wouldn't listen to reason, and he became physically threatening in his gestures and demeanor. He said something about killing me and all other types of horrible things.

Finally the reservationist stuck a note in my hand.

"He said he couldn't wait here for you, but he wants you to call him as soon as possible. This is his phone number."

"What was it that he alleged I had stolen from him?"

"A photograph that he saw this morning on the Granny Goose show. He says you took it out of his house."

I cringed at the thought of having to face this poor angry man because of a stupid photograph that I had shown that morning on the KGMB morning show with host George "Granny Goose" Groves. I loved going on the morning program with Granny, even if I was often booked for 6:00 AM, because he was always funny, pleasant and real. Since his format of interviewing went beyond the two-minute guest spot to promote a book or upcoming event utilized by the other stations, appearing on his program was a good opportunity to "talk story" with him, his crew and the viewing audience who called in with their own stories or questions. In an age of polished, sophisticated television personalities, I enjoyed Granny's informal, rough-at-the-edges style of interviewing.

Yet, I always dreaded being on television because the impact of a ghost story or a comment could reach literally thousands of homes instantaneously for good or ill. Telling a true ghost story isn't like singing a song or telling a fairy tale. A ghost story involves real people interacting with real entities in real places. A person doesn't want to know that their business, building, apartment complex or home is haunted, especially if they are trying to sell or rent the property! If a story is taken in the wrong way or has an untoward impact on a listener, the result can be tremendous anger or fear. Unlike the tour or theater storytelling, where the audience can talk to me later, television sends out an electronic shockwave that has a delayed feedback.

Evidently, the poor staff of TimeWalks felt the brunt of one shockwave that I had sent out that morning when I showed on TV a photograph that had been sent to me in 1973. After giving a talk on Island supernatural traditions at Maui Community College, I received in the mail a photograph of a plantation cottage located in the town of Kahului, Maui. It was an old Kodak color photograph about three by five inches in size, taken, I suspected, in the early 1950s. The note with the photograph was unsigned but, as I recall, said simply, "I heard you give a talk at M.C.C. I've had this for years. Do you see the ghost in the doorway? There was no one standing there when the picture was taken. You may have it. I don't want it."

On closer inspection of the doorway, there did indeed appear to be a shadowy figure standing there, looking out of the old home. Of course, I could not determine whether or not the person who sent the photograph to me had been attempting to "pull my leg." Perhaps there was actually someone at the doorway. Admittedly, when the face of the person was blown up to as large as possible, it was evident that it had no human facial features. It was a stereotypic image of what Hollywood would define as a "phantom." With no way to verify the source or authenticity of the "ghostly photograph," I have over the years simply classified it as an "uncanny" picture. The viewer could make up their own mind as to its supernatural legitimacy.

I was nervous as I called "Bobby," the name of the man who had been outraged by the showing of the "haunted house" photograph. Offending someone was the last thing in the world I wanted to do. I braced myself as the phone was picked up and a voice said, "Hello?"

"Is Bobby there?"

"This is Bobby." His voice was a lot calmer than what I had been anticipating. I winced as I unloaded the bombshell.

"This is Glen Grant. I'm returning your call."

"Oh, yeah. Hi, Glen," he said in an unruffled voice. "I saw you on television this morning. Hey, where did you get that photograph?"

I told him how I received it in the mail in 1973 and how I believed I owned the original photograph.

"Who sent it to you?"

"I'm sorry, there was no name on the letter," I said a little suspiciously. This couldn't be the person in my office who was screaming in the background when I was first informed of a problem by the tour reservationist. He was now simply too emotionless.

"That's really unusual, yeah?" he went on to say calmly. "Because my brother took that photograph when we were both young teenagers. That was the obake house of Kahului. How could you have that photo? It is impossible unless you stole 'em."

"I swear to you I didn't steal the photograph. Do you want to see my original?"

"Sure," he said. "I'll treat you to lunch, okay?"

"No, no. I'll treat you. Where do you want to meet?"

Bobby suggested Jane's Fountain on Liliha Street, which was located just a few blocks from his home. I told him that would be fine and set the time for our luncheon at 1:00 p.m.

"Glen, one more thing, yeah?" my new friend said to me. "I have the power to kill people just by wishing them dead. You understand? You be there, okay?"

I suddenly felt very uneasy as I placed the telephone receiver down. What had been a very nice conversation ended on an extremely enigmatic note.

When I looked up, the entire staff was watching me. Had I been reamed out by Bobby? Was he going to come back and reek havoc? Wasn't he the most enraged person to whom I had ever talked?

"Actually, he was quite nice. We are having lunch together. See you guys, I gotta go."

Have you ever told someone to drop dead, and then they later unexpectedly died? While I fortunately have never been put in a situation where I would seriously wish someone to die, over the years of collecting tales of the uncanny, I have heard a few stories of such unhappy coincidences. I particularly recall one story from a student at the University of Hawai'i who told me how he as a young teenager had chased a ball to a neighbor's yard in a Kailua residential district. This neighbor happened to be a particularly cruel individual who evidently despised children. While the student crawled around in the bushes near the porch looking for the ball, the neighbor came out with a hanger and gave him a stinging swat upon his pants. He ran off, screaming obscenities at the man. Turning suddenly around, he screamed, "I hope you die," ending the sentence with a very descriptive expletive. That night the man had a heart attack and died in his house.

The student was now terrified that he had actually killed the neighbor, but kept his guilt a deeply buried secret. About six months later the father of his good friend had sent him home early, interrupting the kids during some silly game that they had been playing. The student was so angry at being sent home, he muttered, "I hope you die," just under his breath. That night his friend's father passed away from a massive heart attack. Sometimes when he walks down a street, he confided to me with a bit of paranoia, the street lamps over his head go out as if in response to his presence. Now he is very careful what he says to anyone, believing that he can affect their well-being with just his words.

During the entire drive over to Liliha I thought more about Bobby's last line to me about wishing people to death than I did his concern over the photograph. "In the word there is life," I remember a Hawaiian *kupuna* or elder once saying to me, "in the word there is death." This was why it was so important, she explained, to never use words loosely or viciously. "Sticks and stones may break my bones, but words can never hurt me" was not a saying relevant to the oral society of ancient Hawai'i. Words could kill if that was their evil intent.

The most dangerous type of ghost story to tell is the one that sends out into the community wrong or negative impressions of the ancient civilization which is the host to our Islands' multicultural beliefs. For this reason, I have always been very reluctant to ask for, or tell, stories concerning *pule 'ana'ana,* prayers of death or sorcery. First of all, not many people know or are willing to talk about such evil forces that historically have been a part of Hawai'i. Unfortunately, in the last 100 years the notion of praying people to death was also too often associated with *kahuna* who were the keepers of secrets, teachers and healers, not "witch doctors" who spent their time intimidating people, utilizing magic to kill or performing "voodoo." To be "kahuna'd" or "cursed to death" was once a popular vernacular term that erroneously implied only the dark, evil forces in the ancient *ho'omana* or religion, not the spiritual wisdom.

To tell stories of praying people to death would unwittingly encourage, then, too many misconceptions about *kahuna,* both ancient and modern. Not wanting to exacerbate negative impressions which would feed reactions such as "superstitious," "satanic," or "deceitful," I felt it simply would be best to leave all "praying to death" stories out of the *Obake Files.*

On the other hand, to ignore what was obviously a part of the "dark side" of Hawai'i's supernatural heritage would be equally irresponsible, for the power to use prayer to inflict disease or death upon another person has been an integral part of folklore throughout the world. In some cultures the "evil eye," which in effect may be the paranormal phenomenon called psychokinesis, where a person can will an object to levitate or a heart to stop beating, was a form of sorcery involving focused prayer to kill an enemy. "Sympathetic" magic is the belief that the future can be manipulated through the use of physical objects or body parts from the person to be injured. Thus, a lock of hair or scarf that belongs to the intended victim contains a "sympathetic" spiritual connection to its owner. By harming or altering the object, the sorcerer can affect that owner's soul. So-called "voodoo dolls," which are used in the magical rituals of this African-West Indies religion, in many cases must be made with some hair, fingernail, cloth, or personal belonging of the victim to be effective.

Delving into the rituals of *pule 'ana'ana* in ancient Hawai'i reveals that a similar form of "sympathetic" magic was employed in a variety of ways to not only harm the living, but also the family spirits of one's enemy. The intended victim of sorcery could be killed not only with organic parts of his own body, but also through the use of the bones, teeth or hair of his ancestors. For this reason, it was extremely important that the corpse of one's deceased family member should never be found. Disposing of the dead took many forms in ancient Hawai'i, from burying the corpse to concealing the bones in caves or pits. Yet, it was always done in the dark, the location of the bodies or bones a secret that could never be revealed. "They are well hidden from the eyes of men," Hawaiian historian Samuel M. Kamakau wrote in 1870 about the burial places of the ancient people, "and unknown to the 'wizards of the night,' *kupua o ka po,* who might reveal them. These caves hold treasures and other hidden things."

To explain the ritual of *pule 'ana'ana* in a work of this nature is inappropriate. One is directed to "look to the source" for an understanding of this aspect of ancient religious belief in works by such authorities as Samuel M. Kamakau, Davida Malo or Mary Pukui, who, in their writings, sometimes discuss this darker aspect of magic. Suffice to say that there were many forms and prayers of 'ana'ana, several of which were recorded in 1917 by John Emerson. These forms included *ho'opi'opi'o,* a type of magic where the practitioner touched a part of his own body which in turn inflicted pain at the very same place on the victim's body. Ka lawe maunu was described by Emerson as a ritual of burning the clothing of the victim over a three day period after which death would occur. *Ho'ounauna* was a form of sorcery where a message of death was sent directly into the body of the victim. When a sorcerer caught the voice of the victim and used it to kill him, this magic was called *'apo leo. Ke 'oni* magic involved the sorcerer writhing like an eel, which caused his victim to fall down in pain, imitating the motion.

The power of these indigenous priests to manipulate nature through the prayers of *'ana'ana* rivals any of the arts of Merlin from the legends of King Arthur and Camelot. In broad daylight, the *mana* of the prayers of these priests could melt solid rock, bring down thunder and lightning, and set fire to any tree near them during their meditations. Mountains crumbled under the prayers of *'ana'ana,* a grove of trees would wither, a whale could be beached, or a fire brought out of a rock. Whatever they prophesied would come to pass.

The practice of vile magic for the purposes of killing and intimidating others was embraced by only evil people—*'ana'ana* for the purposes of absolution and protecting others from demonic forces was considered a clean and righteous practice conducted by humble people. *Kahuna kuni* was a priest who, through ritual, could heal people being prayed to death, sending the curse back to the source. This priest could use *'ana'ana* if he desired, but he never inflicted disease or death on others unless to return the force to the evil person who had originated it.

According to Kamakau, persons caught stealing *maunu* or "bait" for the purposes of performing *'ana'ana* were severely punished. "Bait" consisted of the hair, clothing, excrement, spittle or any other "sympathetic" object that could be used in magic. Such evil murderers often had their heads cut off with an adz for being caught performing *'ana'ana*—thus, they were called *kahuna 'ana'ana po'oko'i,* "adz-headed *kahuna.*" The bones of such evil people could never be hidden or buried or concealed in caves. Dogs would dig up their bones and drag them into the road, striking fear into the heart of the living to see the defilement resulting from the evil deeds.

Does the power to pray a person to death still exist in modern Hawai'i? Certainly every culture that has settled in the Hawaiian Islands, whether their beliefs be in the form of "stink eye," sorcery or only wishful thinking, has retained some notion of death-dealing prayers. I recall recently sharing some insights on how a "sorcery bundle" with *maunu* or bait was made, quoting from nineteenth century sources. A Hawaiian gentleman in the audience looked at me very sullenly, finally asking how I knew all these things.

"Did you talk to some people in Wai'anae?"

"No," I answered, "my only knowledge comes from books."

"Oh," he replied thoughtfully. "I thought maybe someone told you all that. I was surprised. Because some folks still do that. I didn't think they'd tell you about those things."

Only a few tales of death-dealing prayers have ever been recorded in *The Secret Obake Casebook,* but they are more than enough to keep me far away from deeper knowledge. I am not at all certain whether the traditions revealed through these stories are of Native Hawaiian origin or not. I have no knowledge as to the veracity of the powers or prayers described. As I am a *haole* and a *malihini,* the truth of these truly dark and evil matters will probably be forever hidden from my sight. So, take no cultural information from these tales, infer no wisdom of magical things unseen from the incidents as described. Read these tales merely as a precaution, a fire bell in the night to warn us away from the "image of a nameless god" who, in an ancient prayer of *pule 'ana'ana,* is sent on an errand to

> Bite his throat where it is slender;
> Destroy it and wrench out the jawbone.
> Here is thy gift, a man,
> A long legged fish.
> He descends,
> He goes down to Milu,
> And yet deeper, down to Wakea.
> The hush is ended. It is free.
> The prayer takes its flight.

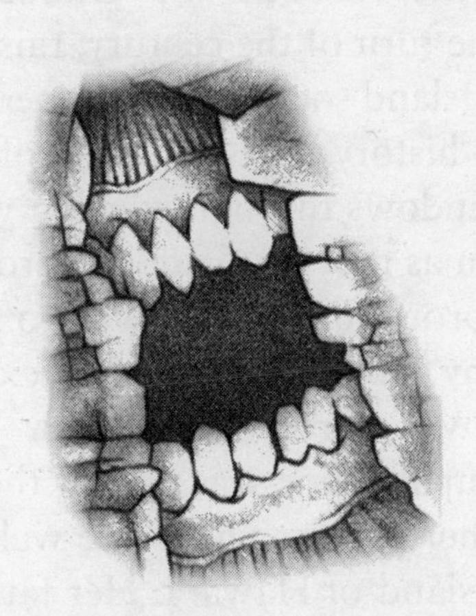

Run, Baby, Run, Run, Run
Casebook Entry #1478

Date of Entry:
May 6, 1986

Supernatural Category:
Sorcery/Prayer Bundle

For two years during 1985-86 I was privileged to travel to the islands of Hawai'i, Kaua'i, Maui and Moloka'i on a regular basis to conduct "oral histories" of senior citizens in a variety of towns and rural settlements. Organized through the University of Hawai'i community college system with support from the Executive Office on Aging, the "Senior Citizen Folklore Project" was, in essence, a great opportunity to "talk story" with a generation whose lives had helped define the "local" multicultural world of their children and grandchildren. Many of these elders had been born at the turn of the century, raised in a plantation world very distant from modern Island society, and tempered by World War II—the greatest conflict in human history. The memories of their parents were especially precious as living windows through which a vista of nineteenth century Hawai'i was faintly seen as moving shadows through the fog of time. The stories they shared—humorous to tragic, bawdy to sublime—have remained indelibly marked upon my storytelling as the textural background upon which I frequently paint my pictures with words.

Martha Pawai of Laupahoehoe was one of those living treasures who would love to talk about her parents who were well-known throughout the Hamakua district on the island of Hawai'i. Her father was a deputy sheriff in the bustling town of Laupahoehoe, which in those days was a vibrant little community with an important, although sometimes dangerous, landing for ships, a post office, stores, churches, a Buddhist temple and hundreds of residents crowded onto a little peninsula of land accessed by a steep and winding road. Her father had a reputation for being a "nice" deputy sheriff since, whenever he caught an escaped Japanese contract laborer who fled the harsh conditions of the nearby sugar plantations, he would let them go rather than collect the bounty. Under the Master and Servants Act, any laborer leaving the plantation would be punished with a mandatory doubling of their length of indentured servitude. Martha's father, he would often tell her, had no stomach for being the haole planters' slave driver.

Martha's mother was an expert *lau hala* weaver who made beautiful mats from the dried and stripped leaves of the pandanus. Martha remembers sleeping as a child on these soft, wide mats that during the day were always rolled up and kept up on a shelf near the ceiling of their home. At night, her parents would bring the *lau hala* mat down, roll it out and Martha and her six siblings would sleep restfully upon its cool fibers. Every Saturday, the family would wipe all the mats clean, the older children polishing the leaves with kerosene. Rubbing kerosene into the shiny *lau hala* helped to preserve its strength and keep the bugs and *'uku,* fleas, away. Her mother was also an accomplished Hawaiian quilter whose unique breadfruit patterns were recognizable through the windward coast of Hawai'i.

Since Martha's father was a deputy sheriff in Laupahoehoe, it was not uncommon for him to be involved in family disputes and other disturbances of the peace. The district was far from being as "wild and woolly" as Waimea in the *paniolo* country was reputed to be, but *pilikia* did occasionally come to Hamakua. When Martha was 12 years old, the *pilikia* blew up one weekend, when a drunken brawl broke out between a group of rowdy men in the small village saloon. Martha's father was a huge Hawaiian-*haole* man over six feet tall with a jet-black, handlebar mustache, stern countenance and a large, white Stetson hat. He strolled into the saloon, picked up the drunken brawlers by the scruff of their necks and threw them into the road, using a black snakewhip on their backsides. When one Hawaiian fellow tried to fight back, Martha's father used his Colt .45 to pistol-whip him nearly to death. After that incident, no one ever tried to talk sassy to the deputy sheriff of Laupahoehoe.

The family of the pistol-whipped ruffian let it be known that the deputy sheriff was not their favorite person. There was some talk that the man's brothers were going to gang up on Martha's father, who brushed that kind of talk off with a raised eyebrow and a guffaw. Like with a lot of bullies, there was more bark than bite in their threats. In fact, the sullen, beaten young man always gave a wide berth to the deputy sheriff whenever they ran into each other in the town.

One day a few months later, Martha was playing ball with her brother in their yard. Her brother's high pitch went over her head and the little homemade baseball rolled under the house. Since their cottage was set up about six inches from the ground on stilts so that in case of high tide the home would be safe, Martha could crawl under the structure to fetch her ball. Her father had stored a few things under the house, so she had to inch her way around them, groping for the missing baseball. When she finally found it, she saw that it had come to rest against a large, unusual package that was hidden under the house. Curious, she not only retrieved the ball, but the container, which she brought out into the daylight.

"What you got there, baby?" asked her uncle. He had just ridden up on his horse as she was crawling out from under the house with her "package." Uncle Keli'i was actually Martha's great-uncle on her mother's family side. A skilled fisherman who was raised at Waipi'o valley to the north, he had come to live with his niece and her family in his old age. He took the bulky object from Martha and, for the first time in her life, she saw her uncle's usually genial face suddenly wrinkle in a very somber frown.

"You found this under the house?"

"What is it, Uncle?"

"A *pu'olo,* baby," he whispered. "A bundle of death."

In the daylight, she could see that the bundle was woven from little fibers that she knew as the 'ie'ie vines that grew luxuriantly in the upper valleys at high elevation. The package was about two cubic feet in size and didn't seem to have a top or bottom. Suddenly, Martha noticed that the *pu'olo* was moving in her uncle's hands, as if something inside it was alive!

"Baby," Uncle Keli'i said, "you have to hold it. Don't be afraid, take it in your hands."

"It's moving!" she protested. "I can't touch it!"

"Hurry, now," he insisted. "Hurry, hurry, hurry, you take it."

At her uncle's insistence, Martha carried the *pu'olo* in her arms as he led her across the yard, out into the woods and located a large *pu hala* or pandanus tree. As she was running after her Uncle Keli'i, she could feel the bundle stirring, things inside it moving about within the tight weaving. She prayed that whatever it was wouldn't escape. Her uncle ordered her to put the bundle next to the pandanus tree.

"Now let's go eat lunch," Uncle told her. "We'll take care of this after lunch."

She could hardly eat her lunch, her stomach was so upset. What had Uncle meant that this thing was a "bundle of death?" Where had it come from? What was inside it that was moving?

Uncle Keli'i never fully explained to his grand-niece what was inside the *pu'olo* until a few years later when she was a young woman and he felt that she was old enough to understand. These bundles contained *maunu,* or bait, he later told her, objects that perhaps had been stolen from the family. Neither her uncle nor she dared to open the package, but he thought it may contain a little toy, a piece of clothing, possibly some hair or other items obtained about the house. Inside the bundle could also be chicken feathers or animal body parts from livestock the family owned. Once as a child, he told Martha, he also had come across a *pu'olo.* In his ignorance, he had actually opened it to find that it contained chicken feathers which flew out, covering his flesh. They attached themselves to his arm and remained there, unable to be pulled off, until his father chanted a pule kuni, a prayer to reverse a death prayer, sending it back to its originator. Thus, the objects inside the bundle were not inanimate, but stirred to life through prayer.

The prayers of *'ana'ana* began with the sorcerer appealing to his *'aumakua* in the four directions of the earth, the ocean, and the heavens. Then the prayers were directed to invoke Uliiuka, Uliikai, Ulinanapono, and Ulinanahewa. In one such prayer, the sorcerer chants:

For a life, a death,
A great *ka'upu* bird is calling,
Sounding nearby, calling out.
What is the food it is calling for?
A man is the food it is calling for.
Thunder cracks in the heavens,
The earth quakes.

Your legs bend,
Your hands become paralyzed,
Your back hunches,
Your neck is twisted,
Your head breaks open,
Your liver rots,
Your intestines fall to pieces.

Someone, Uncle Keli'i later explained to Martha, wished this family to be harmed through sorcery. The *pu'olo* placed under the house would eventually bring sickness and death to all blood relations, often the young and innocent being the first victims. At night a choking sensation would come to the throat of the living, their body paralyzed and unable to defend themselves. Night after night, this choking, pressing sensation would return until the person would be found dead in their bed, a victim of *pule 'ana'ana.* As another death prayer says in English:

> Numbness, numbness, numbness, numbness,
> Spreads, spreads, spreads, spreads,
> Stiffens, stiffens, stiffens, stiffens;
> Your head droops, droops, droops,
> Bends over, bends over,
> It droops, droops.
>
> His eyes droop,
> His nose droops,
> His mouth droops,
> His neck droops. . . . .

Martha would learn these things from Uncle Keli'i much later. That day, he told her very little, except that, to protect her family, she must do exactly as he instructed. When lunch was over at about 3 o'clock that afternoon, Uncle told her it was time to take care of the bundle. They returned to the *pu hala* tree, fetched the evil package, and began a journey on horseback up the Laupahoehoe road to a place high above the steep cliffs overlooking a wild, storm-tossed sea. It was nearly sunset when Martha and her uncle finally arrived at the isolated location. Dismounting from her horse, she followed Uncle to the edge of the precipice, all the while clutching the moving bundle.

"See out there, baby," Uncle told her, "where the sea is angry? You must throw this thing out there, as far away from you as you can. After you throw it, then you must turn and run away. And don't look back."

Doing as Uncle Keli'i instructed, she stood on the edge of the cliff and hurled the *pu'olo* as far as she could into the churning sea, hundreds of feet below. She didn't wait to see what would happen, but turned to run as her uncle had advised. However, as she was running away from the cliff, there was a sudden loud explosion, like a charge of dynamite had been set off! Startled, she stopped running and turned around to see a whirlwind rising up from the sea, lifting above the steep cliffs like a waterspout ascending into the heavens.

"Run, baby!" Uncle now screamed wildly, "I told you run! Don't look back! Run, baby, run, run, run, run!"

The wind chased her as she scurried to a large guava tree about 100 feet in the distance. The wind swirled around her violently, as she heard the chanting of her uncle in the distance, attempting to send the malevolent force back into the ocean. Sucking her back towards the cliff, the wind taunted and pulled upon her, dragging her back into its evil grip as she struggled against the force, until she was able to grab the tree. Clinging to it for her life, she slowly felt the force diminish until, at last, the wind died. "Thunder cracks in the heavens; the earth quakes."

When she returned to the place where she had thrown the bundle into the sea, she looked down to see a great hole along the shore where the *pu'olo* had hit and exploded. For it is said that, when one throws these bundles of death away, they literally blow up when they strike the earth, as if they are filled with nitroglycerin. Thus can concentrated human evil and hatred placed inside these packages render death and destruction on a supernatural proportion.

Then, as Martha gazed down into that horrible pit, she heard screaming coming from the hole—horrible, screeching human wails that poured forth from the dark abyss to fill the twilight evening sky.

"Devils, baby," said Uncle solemnly. "Do you hear the devils? There are devils down there, screaming."

"Mr. Grant," Martha then said softly, "do you want to see the hole? It's still there. I can show you."

A few of the senior citizens, Martha and myself eagerly took the ride from Papa'aloa where the "oral history" session had been conducted to the beach park at Laupahoehoe. Along the way, Martha explained that the family of the angry, pistol-whipped man had sent the prayers of death against her family to get revenge for what her father had done to him. Uncle Keli'i noted that within a day of the disposal of the bundle into the sea, that family suffered a great tragedy. The grandfather broke his neck in a fall from his horse. The death prayer had been reversed.

All of her friends then started asking her why she had never told them this story before. They all knew the hole to which she was referring, but none of them could remember how it had gotten there.

"You never asked me to tell you these kinds of stories," Martha sweetly said. "Mr. Grant asked."

The village which Martha's father had once watched over as the deputy sheriff was now a quiet little residential area with a few homes, a large playground and beach park and a melancholy shrine to the teachers and students killed by the tidal wave that hit on April 1, 1946. Martha showed us where her family home had once stood before the devastation of the *tsunami* which had destroyed Laupahoehoe. From the boat landing at the rugged shore, Martha pointed to the place where the *pu'olo* had hit the earth from the cliffs above, a rocky shoreline site which I maneuvered by myself, carefully stepping and leaping from boulder to boulder.

When I finally found the hole, it was exactly as Martha had described—a gaping cavity in the earth created by what seemed to be a massive explosion. Of course, I thought to myself, this could have been made by a construction crew utilizing sticks of dynamite many years before when the area was still used as a landing. I never actually witnessed a bundle of *maunu*, evil bait, blowing up. However, as I looked down into that pit, trying to imagine that moment now over 75 years ago when the devils of Hell called out for their victims, I couldn't help but feel a little terror at the sinister mysteries both natural and supernatural that shroud our lives.

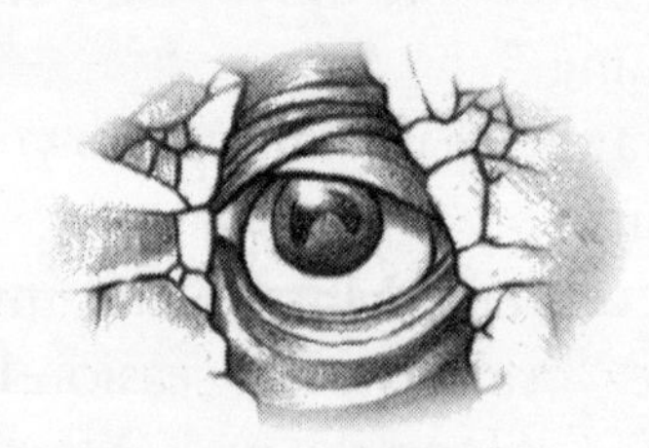

No Cause of Death on Maui
Casebook Entry #1378

Date of Entry:
July 20, 1995

Supernatural Category:
Sorcery/Family Curse

Is there such a thing as a "family curse?"

When the people of Hawai'i were once more tightly bound to one another in their small-town communities, rural camps or urban neighborhoods, it was not unusual for disputes to arise between families which sometimes became lasting bitter feuds that never seemed to fade away. The *aloha* which imperceptibly flows through the lives of people interdependent upon one another can also turn to a hatred that festers like a cancer on the soul of a family. In a community rich with supernatural folkways, this unbridled hatred can easily be used as the power to place a curse upon another person which, through the generations, may be carried by a family.

In the 1960s, for example, two second-generation Japanese-American men, lifelong friends, had a falling out that became intensely hateful as each cursed the other openly among their mutual acquaintances. The original dispute had been actually very minor, but their disappointment in each other became so intense that it had turned to unadulterated contempt. It wasn't uncommon to hear one of the men wish the other one dead.

The wife of one of the men told me that the day the news came that his rival had actually died, her husband openly gloated that he had outlived the other "bastard." His foolish pride at his former friend's death, however, quickly turned to horror that night when, as he was reading his newspaper in the living room, he began to suddenly gag. Rushing to the assistance of her husband, who had collapsed under the newspaper, the wife was terrified to see that he was having a massive heart attack. Fortunately, he was rushed to the hospital in time to save his life, although one side of his body was badly paralyzed, requiring him to use ambulatory crutches for the rest of his life.

The family was convinced that the heart attack was a "curse" put upon him by the spirit of his rival, because following the heart attack red welts in the form of long finger marks were clearly visible on his neck for several hours after he was rushed to the emergency room.

At 'Amauulu camp in Hilo, an area nicknamed "Hollywood Hills" because it is on a steep, sloping rise, rumors persisted in the 1960s about a curse between two Japanese women. A woman who lived at the bottom of the hill had evidently been very jealous for some reason of a woman who lived at the top of the hill. The jealousy and hatred increased, until it was widely believed that the woman at the bottom of the hill had put a curse on the other. From that time forward, people taking food up to 'Amauulu camp to visit the cursed woman could never arrive fast enough that the food wasn't always spoiled!

When a young Portuguese man was in the fourth grade, growing up on Maui, he had been very hateful of another boy who had been very good in sports. One afternoon, he explained to me, his closest friend and he went over to the home of the boy's grandfather and stuck pins into the head and heart of a little doll that they had made resembling their rival. They had seen the "voodoo" doll technique on *The Alfred Hitchcock Show* on television and believed it could work against the boy. To "localize" the technique, he told me that he said a Portuguese curse that he had heard his grandmother use against another woman, spilling chicken blood over the doll's head.

Although he admitted to me that he and his friend had no idea what they were doing, he suddenly became disturbed that it was wrong. Wishing to stop the ritual, they decided to burn the doll. As the flames consumed the tiny, evil object, they became even more frightened to see the head with pins and chicken blood burning. They stomped the fire out, dug a deep hole and buried the badly burned "voodoo" doll. They swore to each other they would never say another word to anyone about what happened.

Over the next months, nothing happened to the other boy, who continued to excel in sports and get good grades. In the ensuing years, they all went on to graduate from high school, the boy they had hated graduating with honors. The curse of the doll had evidently not affected his victim's life whatsoever. However, a few years after everyone had gone their separate ways, the Portuguese young man was at the Ala Moana Shopping Center when he heard his name called out. There was the boy whom he had tried to curse many years earlier, limping towards him. Right after graduation, with a scholarship to play baseball at a mainland school, he had been involved in a terrible automobile accident that horribly scarred one side of his body, leaving his left leg crippled. As much as I suggested to the Portuguese young man that his act of hatred many years earlier probably had nothing to do with this poor man's accident, he could not be convinced, feeling a horrible guilt and shame that he had ruined this man's life over some childhood prank. The curse had come back to plague the person who had sent it.

Noelani Akina believed that she carried a "family curse," although she wasn't certain of its origin. I met Noelani when she was a "living history" trainee in a program I was teaching for at a large tourist destination site on the island of Maui. The tropical plantation site offered visitors a wealth of information on the exotic fruits of Hawai'i, but very little on the history of the various people who once worked on the plantations. In an effort to create a "mini-Colonial Williamsburg," the management asked if I would train the tour guide staff on the techniques of "living history" so that ,when they showed people around the grounds, they could become the characters of the past.

A variety of techniques were used during the training to improve the guides' ability to tell stories and make dramatic presentations. Since all of the staff were virtually born and raised on Maui, and represented nearly every major ethnic group of the plantation, I suggested that they personalize their presentations by "becoming" their grandparents. Each of them did extensive research on their family history, selected a character to become, and successfully brought history to life. Not only would the visitors benefit from the cultural perspectives re-created by the guide, but the guides themselves had personally benefited from the effort to connect with their family heritage.

One of the most enjoyable aspects of the training was the storytelling sessions where each guide would practice telling a family tale. Noelani's story that day was very short, but she had just heard it from her great-aunt who had told her that the Akina family carried a curse. This curse had been put upon them many years ago by a Portuguese woman who had been angry at Noelani's great-grandmother. In retaliation for some harm done to her, the woman's curse has killed every dog the Akina family has ever owned. To this day, Noelani and all of her siblings cannot own a dog longer than a month because it dies of an illness or an accident.

"It is so strange, yeah," she told me after the training, "that my family would have that kind of curse? I never really noticed it before until my aunty told me. Growing up, my father never let our family own a dog. That was kind of strange, because we lived in Makawao, where everyone had all kinds of animals. Since I got married, my husband and kids have wanted dogs. But they always died. I asked my sisters and they said that it's true. Their dogs haven't lived longer than a month. Strange, yeah?"

She went on to say that her grandaunt had hinted that there may have been a death involved in the origin of the curse—that the Portuguese woman's husband had died in a freak accident and she felt that Noelani's great-grandmother was to blame.

"Do you think there would be any way to find out how he died?"

"You'll need to know his name and when the accident occurred," I advised her. "If it wasn't too many years ago, maybe the Maui police would have a record."

Two weeks later I returned to Maui for a training session, and Noelani indicated that, if I didn't mind, she'd like to drive me back to the airport in the afternoon. As she gave me the lift, she excitedly told me the news that she had finally pried out of her grandaunt. The family that had cursed them was named Camacho. The man who had died had been a dogcatcher for Maui county back in the 1930s, when the accident took place. Her grandaunt had said that she sincerely knew nothing else beyond that. In those days, both families had been very tight-lipped about the bad blood between them, great-grandmother taking the secret of the Akina family to the grave. The Portuguese woman who had put out the curse had also died.

Noelani asked if I had enough information to find out the facts surrounding the dogcatcher's death. I promised that, if I could find the time, I'd check out the State Archives in Honolulu for any records they may have for Maui county in the 1930s. However, I strongly suggested that Noelani not build up her expectations—I would probably be able to find out very little. After all, the position of dogcatcher in the 1930s was not a major administrative post in the government records.

And I was absolutely right. Although the State of Hawai'i Archives contains all official records for the Territory of Hawai'i during the period between 1900 and 1959, the details of the death of a dogcatcher was evidently not documented in any government records which I could identify. However, when I looked at the obituaries for the 1930s, I discovered there were not very many "Camacho" listed. In a few hours I had a list of the dates of death of about 20 persons whose surname was Camacho who died during this 10 year period.

The next step was going through the microfilm of *The Honolulu Advertiser* and *Honolulu Star-Bulletin* to see if the deaths of these individuals were reported in the O'ahu newspapers. Usually a small notice of individuals who had died on the other islands was listed by the family of the deceased, especially if that person may have had relatives on O'ahu. When I looked at the newspapers on the date of death of the sixth name on the list, I hit pay dirt.

"Duke Camacho died instantly last Thursday evening at Puunene on Maui after his truck went out of control and hit a tree. Camacho was a dog-catcher with the county of Maui." The obituary went on to list the name of his wife and four surviving children. The date of his death was July 19, 1939.

Getting the actual death certificate of Duke Camacho was more problematic. Neither Noelani or I were descendants of the deceased, and I figured that there would be a reluctance to release such private information by the Board of Health. I was again absolutely right. To obtain a death certificate required verification that we were kin of Duke Camacho. I called Noelani with the news that I had been stumped right at the point of unraveling the cause of death. Did she know any one of the Camachos who could give her some assistance? She thanked me profusely for all that I had uncovered and said that she would see if any of her friends knew anyone named Camacho.

It took several days and quite a few calls, but finally it turned out that a friend of a friend did indeed know someone who had been born at Pu'unene whose surname was Camacho. This person turned out to be Steve Camacho, Duke Camacho's great-nephew and a salesman with a local automobile distributor. Steve was very friendly to Noelani, confessing to her that he had never even heard of the feud between the Camacho and Akina families. All he knew about Duke Camacho was that he was dead. Since he was, as far as he knew, the only Camacho left living on Maui related to the former dogcatcher, he agreed to help Noelani find out how his granduncle had died. He signed all the authorization papers with the Board of Health proving his direct relationship to the deceased, sent in his duplication fee, and a few weeks later received the official document. After reading it, Noelani called me immediately.

"'The cause of death of Duke Camacho,'" Noelani read to me over the telephone, "'is unknown. The body was in an unusually advanced state of decomposition.' What does that mean, Glen?"

"I don't know," I told her. "I'm not a doctor. But I thought he was in a truck accident."

"It says here 'cause of death unknown.' Maybe he died when he was driving the truck and then it hit the tree."

I told Noelani that, even to this day, the cause of death is not always determined even despite all the tools of modern science. But the fact that the body was in a state of advanced decomposition was to me most unusual. Had they not found his remains for some time?

"What is the date and time of the autopsy?" I asked Noelani.

"July 19, 1939. 11:00 p.m."

The date of the accident was July 19, 1939. The time of the accident was not in the newspaper, but I wondered how long the body would need to be exposed to the elements for an autopsy at 11:00 PM to determine that it was in a state of "advanced decomposition." If Duke Camacho had been baking in a hot Maui sun, maybe the rate of deterioration had been accelerated.

A medical textbook, I concluded, would be an excellent place to start to understand more about a subject which some readers may at this point wish to skip. I consulted John Glaister and Edgar Rentoul's *Medical Jurisprudence and Toxicology* for clarification on the nature of decomposition. The authors suggested that the rate of deterioration is dependent upon a variety of factors. Sometimes a body will decompose very fast, becoming a skeleton in only a few weeks. In other cases, it could be preserved indefinitely. The rates are quickened due to the presence of air, moisture, microorganisms, moderate temperatures, and insects. The following are the progressive signs of putrefaction:

- Greenish color over the whole of the abdomen and other parts of the body.
- Discoloration and swelling of the face.
- Distension of the abdomen with gases.
- Brownish coloration of the surface veins giving an arborescent pattern on the skin.
- Development of blisters of varying size on the surface of the body.
- Bursting of the blisters, and denudation of large irregular surfaces due to the shedding of the skin.
- Escape of blood-stained fluid from the mouth and nostrils.
- Liquefaction of the eyeballs.
- Increasing discoloration of the body generally, and greater and progressive abdominal distension.
- Presence of maggots.
- Shedding of the nails, and loosening of the hair.
- Facial features unrecognizable.
- Conversion of tissues into a semi-fluid mass.
- Bursting open of the abdominal and thoracic cavities.
- Progressive dissolution of the body.

While no timetable is given as to how long this putrefaction process would need to take place to reach a state of advanced decomposition, even a piece of raw meat left out on a kitchen sink requires a day or two before it turns green and produces maggots. Instead of solving our mystery, the receipt of the death certificate only intensified our curiosity about the curse between the Camacho and Akina families.

The next time I visited Maui to conduct training, Noelani and I met earlier to visit the humane society facilities to ask if anyone there knew anybody who may have worked as a dogcatcher in the 1930s. Duke Camacho must have had friends. No one at the center, which is now responsible for maintaining the dog and cat population on Maui, could help us, but one person gave us the name of a retired county dogcatcher who still occasionally volunteered his services to the humane society. While he had started his job back in the 1950s and couldn't really help us, he gave us the name of a Chinese-Hawaiian gentleman by the name of Chock who lived now in Kula. He was one of the real old-timers, the retiree told us, from back in the days before the war.

Henry Chock wasn't listed in the telephone directory, so Noelani and I drove out to Kula hoping that the old fellow hadn't passed away. Through asking someone at a little country store in this upcountry Maui district, we learned that a Henry Chock lived two houses past a big monkeypod tree about a mile up the road. At first we weren't certain we had found the right house, but, when a gang of dogs of all sizes and varieties ran out to greet us, whelping and jumping all over us, we figured we may have come close to the residence of a dogcatcher. The yard was strewn with all kinds of objects which the dogs regularly chewed upon. The smell of dog doodoo was pungent from the many piles of unattended droppings that littered the ground. Two old, abandoned, rust-covered automobiles from the 1950s were junked under a jungle of vines and weeds.

Mr. Chock was an elderly, thin little man with a very stooped back who leaned more to his Chinese than his Hawaiian ancestry. His snow-white head of hair framed a face that seemed set in perpetual scowl. Obviously he wasn't the nicest man in Kula, as he barked when he spoke to us, but at least he didn't chase us off when we told him that we had come to "talk story" about a fellow named Duke Camacho. He looked at me askance, smiled weakly at Noelani, and invited us into his living room which also served as a kennel for his pack of little beasts. The dogs waltzed gingerly ahead of us into the ill-kept room, each finding a resting place on one of the couches, chairs or floor. A cute little poi dog with little control of his salivating glands put his head on my lap after I sat down on the couch. The smell of dog hair was overwhelming throughout the house. Mr. Chock plopped himself down into an old rattan chair with frayed cushions and asked Noelani what we wanted to know about Duke Camacho.

First, Noelani explained how she had recently discovered from her great-aunt that there may have been a curse put on her family by Duke Camacho's wife. Since she could remember, she told him, her immediate family had never been able to keep a dog alive for longer than a month. All of this had to do, we suspected, with her great-grandmother and Duke Camacho sometime back in the 1930s. One of the former dogcatchers said that Mr. Chock may have been around back then.

He listened intently, nodding and gently gnawing the back of his jaw as if he were chewing his cud. When Noelani finished, he spoke.

"I remember your great-grandmother. You don't look anything like her. She was frightening."

"Really?" Noelani said, a bit puzzled. She had never met or even seen a picture of her great-grandmother, but had assumed she was a sweet woman from what grandmother had once told her.

"I'll never forget the day I first saw her. I was with Mr. Camacho, driving through Pu'unene camp in his old Ford truck. The one he later died in."

I suddenly could see Henry Chock, then a 25-year-old man struggling to find a job during the tough years of the Depression, finally getting paid to accompany an old Portuguese dogcatcher in his simple daily duties keeping the wild dog population under control on the plantations. The old beaten-up Ford truck bounced along a semi-paved road through the plantation camps where the various groups in Pu'unene had been ethnically divided. I could see the truck turning into a long, sugar cane lined road through the plantation fields, coming to a place where a large dog covered in mange started to run along side barking at the front wheel of the truck. The old dog's body was like a patch quilt, as large pieces of hair had fallen out, leaving squares of pink flesh exposed.

Duke Camacho stopped the truck, pulled out his rifle from the back, loaded a single bullet into the chamber and, as that mange-covered dog pranced around them, barking, he shot it right between the eyes, killing it instantly. One thing Mr. Camacho never tolerated was diseased dogs running around, spreading its skin disorder to other animals, Henry explained. After the dog had been killed, Henry dutifully got out of the truck, grabbed the animal by its two hind legs and swung the carcass unceremoniously into the back of the truck.

The Ford engine fired up, as the two men ambled along in the truck another 200 yards or so when an old, wild-eyed, pupule lady, Noelani's great-grandmother, leaped into the road. Her long, yellowish-white hair flew in all directions and her eyes were red with hatred.

"WHY YOU SHOOT MY DOG!" she screamed at the top of her lungs, pointing her finger at Mr. Camacho.

Not intimidated by the old lady's anger, Mr. Camacho stuck his head out the window of his door and screamed back at her.

"YOUR DOG HAD MANGE, LADY! GOT ANYMORE? I'LL SHOOT THEM ALL!"

With that, he let off the hand brake, put the truck into gear and rolled forward as if to hit the woman. She ran to the side of the road and kept screaming something at them like, "You'll pay. You'll pay." Out the back window Henry saw Noelani's great-grandmother turn her fist to the heavens, cursing the universe and all dogcatchers in it.

The very next day, Henry Chock continued, was Saturday. Old Duke Camacho loved to drink his *'okolehao*. He made the best pineapple swipes in Pu'unene. Since it was pau hana and tomorrow was church day, Mr. Camacho decided to have a few drinks before going home. He and Henry shared a bottle of homemade swipes until about 8:00 PM. They got into the Ford truck to go home, but Mr. Camacho was too drunk to drive. Henry got behind the wheel and was just pulling out into the road when the senior dog-catcher seemed to collapse, like he just fainted. His head went right into the dashboard with a thud and Henry tried to catch him with his one free hand, figuring that he had had too much to drink. In trying to grab Mr. Camacho, Henry lost control of the steering wheel as the truck rolled into the tree only going about five mph. Nobody was hurt as he tried to wake his boss up. There was no response from Duke Camacho, as if his spirit had just gone out of his body.

At this point, Mr. Chock stopped his story and took a long, hard look at Noelani.

"You sure you want to hear the rest, young lady?" His brown eyes seemed to be piercing into her flesh. "It wasn't very nice."

"Go on," Noelani insisted. We hadn't come this far to stop now.

I have no idea how many times over the years Henry Chock had told this story. But, from his demeanor and reaction to the tale, it seemed this may have been the first time in nearly 50 years. This wasn't something that you told for amusement as a ghost story. It was a secret you kept hidden until the time in your old age when a young woman with the blood of those involved finally asks, "Can you tell me the truth?"

In trying to awake Mr. Camacho, Henry noticed that a pimple on the back of the dogcatcher's neck was large and inflamed. Suddenly it burst, the white pus literally pouring out in a little stream as something wiggled out of the tiny cavity on his neck. In the pus was a maggot inching its way out of Mr. Camacho's flesh, followed by another and then another. Horrified, Henry pulled the body back from the dashboard as the head tilted back onto the front seat. With Duke Camacho's frozen, open-eyed gaze staring at the ceiling of the truck cabin, maggots came crawling out of his gaping mouth, from his nostrils and from his ears. The tiny white worms that breed within putrefied flesh were feasting upon the brains of Mr. Camacho, as Henry fled into the bushes, vomiting until he began to retch blood out of his guts.

The sheriff never believed Henry when he told the authorities later that night what had happened. They were convinced that the accident happened sometime that morning, that Duke Camacho had been killed when his head struck against the dashboard and the decomposed head was the result of baking in a hot sun. Certainly the front of the Ford wasn't too damaged, and there was no serious wound on Mr. Camacho's head. The autopsy done that night could not determine the exact cause of death. Henry Chock had no prior record of arrest, no motive to murder his boss, and there was no evidence of homicide. Therefore, the news was released that the dogcatcher had died in a car accident. Period. Case closed.

Henry had not gone back to the cabin of the truck at all, even after the police arrived. He only heard later from one of the men at the scene that when they lifted Duke Camacho's body out of the cabin, the stench of his corpse was so pilau, it smelled several days old. Broken blisters covered his body, as large sections of his epidermis were missing. He had been eaten alive by the elements.

During the wake and funeral, Duke Camacho's casket was closed. This was very difficult for a religious, Catholic family of Portuguese background who wanted to view the body as a process of mourning. No embalmer could touch it. The corpse was beyond cosmetic repair. This especially hurt Mrs. Camacho, who openly cursed the woman who she believed had prayed her husband to death.

"I never saw your great-grandmother again," Mr. Chock said to Noelani, "but everyone in Puʻunene knew after this that she was one of the 'Evil Ones.'"

"An 'Evil One?'" I asked.

"Someone who is filthy and foul and uses *pule ʻanaʻana.* You heard of that? Portuguese got powerful curses too, you know. I heard that Mrs. Camacho had a lady do some really terrible things with a chicken and pig, rituals that no decent Portuguese would talk about. Secret things. And your great-grandmother went *make* right after."

Noelani was now crying, hearing these terrible things said against her own ancestor. I had heard about the "Evil Ones" before, from other informants who claimed that there were people in their villages in the early days of the century who were feared as practitioners of praying to death. When these people cast their evil spells, I was told by eyewitnesses, they could literally walk right up a wall and then hang upside down from the ceiling! When they died, the maggots that they had put into their victims breed in their living flesh. At their funerals, the insects would be released, pouring from every cavity of the "Evil One's" corpse.

There was really nothing more that Henry Chock could tell us, so we thanked him for his time and made the drive back to Wailuku. Noelani and I had started this little research project in the hope of learning more about why dogs seemed to die prematurely in her family. We may have even at some moments in our journey felt excited or thrilled by the adventure of the hunt. Now that we had found what we were looking for, both of us were saddened and frightened. Could such things really be?

I advised her that she may not want to pursue any more details on her great-grandmother's life, but she seemed determined to find out more. Maybe she wanted to vindicate her, to see if there was any truth to these rumors which had been passed on to us by Mr. Chock. This was her own business, I assured her. This dark skeleton in her family closet she would need to exorcise on her own. I wished her luck and returned to Honolulu.

A few days after our conversation with Henry Chock, I was "looking to the source" one more time to grasp the connection between ancient mysteries and modern occurrences. In one of Samuel M. Kamakau's essays on sorcery, he records another *pule ʻanaʻana* intended to invoke Uli. I reread the English translation over and over trying to fathom its meaning and possible connection to the events of 1939:

Arise, O Kama! Break open the front!

Arise, O Kama! Break open the head, O Kama!

Seize the victim, O Kama!

The maggots crawl in your head, O victim!

Seize the victim, O Kama!

Maggots bunch together in your eyes, O victim,
Your mouth is eaten by maggots, O victim,
Your mouth rots away with maggots, O victim;
Disease breaks through your throat, O victim.
It is broken through by maggots, eaten by maggots;
Maggots itch in your throat, O victim!

Crawl, O maggots; itch, O maggots;
Eat, O maggots; root, O maggots;
Disembowel, O maggots, the victim!
You are rotten with maggots,
O victim who is seized fast!
You are slow, O victim,
You are rotten; you are changed!

There was one more training session on Maui before the plantation's "living history" program opened to rave reviews and then died a quick death a few months later. History evidently is interesting to those of us in search of an understanding of family curses, but it didn't sell enough pineapples to warrant its continued presentation at a commercial tourist site. The place reverted to the selling of tropical fruits, tee shirts, plastic cups and logo caps as the historical re-creations were abandoned.

As far as Noelani Akina was concerned, I never heard from her again. I only prayed that, for her sake, she finally was able to make peace with the ghosts and demons of her past.

When I arrived at Jane's Fountain in Liliha, "Bobby" was already waiting for me. A tall, local man of mixed ancestry in a bright blue golf cap with a logo for a Maui hotel, wearing shorts, rubber slippers and a Merrie Monarch Hula Festival tee shirt, Bobby shook my hand politely and apologized for how he had talked to the TimeWalks staff.

"I was just so upset when I saw you on Granny Goose this morning. I really thought you stole my picture. I didn't know you had your own."

We found a booth in this classic old Honolulu cafe with high wood seats, a soda fountain right out of "Happy Days," aged advertisements from the fifties still hanging on the wall, and an atmosphere that literally breathes Hawai'i. Bobby ordered the *oyako donburi* which he claimed was the best in the Islands, while I had the chicken long rice plate. As we waited for our lunches, out of a plastic Star Market shopping bag he pulled a yellowed manila envelope, which was closed with rusted staples. On the envelope was written a date, "November 2, 1955." He pulled out the staples, opened the envelope and brought out its contents.

Inside was the photograph of what he again identified as the obake house of Kahului with the strange, faceless figure at the door. It was identical to the one I owned, which we placed next to his on the diner's Formica tabletop. They were exactly alike. The only difference between my print and his was that he owned the negative. I examined it carefully in the sunlight. It was indeed the negative for the photograph.

"My brother died not long after taking this picture," he again explained to me, "so I've always kept it hidden. This picture is very bad luck. No one should make copies of it. I don't know how you got this picture, but I have to warn you. My cousin borrowed it from me once to make a print and, on the day he went to pick it up at the photo shop, he had a car accident and broke his back. He still needs to use a cane. No good comes from this photo."

I assured him that I would be careful. While I said I wasn't certain that I believed in supernatural "curses" affixed to objects, I was very, very respectful.

"This picture also gave me the power to kill people," he then said bluntly. "I can kill them just by telling them to die."

I wasn't certain I wanted to hear too much about this part of his story, but he was adamant that, on at least four occasions since acquiring this photograph he had been directly responsible for the death of people whom he didn't like. Each of them had done something either very wrong to him or to someone else whom he loved. In each case, the person dropped dead right in front of him.

"I was working construction one day," Bobby explained, "and I heard this man say something to me about being a stupid Hawaiian. I told him stop calling me names, but he did it again. He said something racist against Hawaiians. He was standing right next to a large crane operator when I said to him, 'Die, you bastard.' At that second an electrical wire overhead snapped, fell to the metal frame of the crane and electrocuted the man, who was resting his hand on the machinery while standing in a puddle of rainwater. His ears and feet smoked like he was frying."

He went on to tell me how his former boss, a landlord and a neighbor had also all died, though not quite so dramatically, within one week of his telling them to 'Die, you bastard!" This picture had given him this incredible power to inflict death on people.

I didn't want to ask much more about his power to kill people just by using three words, but concentrated on the chicken long rice, quietly and politely finishing my lunch as quickly as possible. All I could think of as he was telling his story was the outburst that the staff described at the office earlier in the morning. Did he harbor any resentment or hatred for me? Had he understood that I never stole his photo, but innocently received it from someone on Maui who indicated to me that I could use it? I hate grown men and women who beg forgiveness on their hands and knees, but I was willing to kiss Bobby's feet if I needed to. I have never felt so paranoid in my life while eating chicken long rice.

I quickly picked up the check that the waitress brought to the table, making sure that Bobby didn't want dessert or some coffee after his meal. I paid the bill for both lunches and, with a big smile, asked as humbly as I could if everything was all right with him now.

"Yeah, I'm not mad at you."

With a sigh of relief I stood up to leave, assuring him that if I ever used the picture again, I'd be sure to give his brother credit. I was just about to go out the door when he called after me in a loud, angry voice.

"Wait! I forgot something."

Checking for electrical wiring around me which may be dangerously close, I held my breath and turned around.

"Yes?"

"I forgot to ask you to sign my *Obake Files* for my wife. She really liked the book."

I wrote a very friendly note "To the Wife of My Good Friend Bobby," signed my name and, with a final sigh of relief, left the man who could kill with only words quietly finishing a cup of coffee in that marvelous time warp called Jane's Fountain. One more "frightful fiend" had been cast out of the shadows behind me, as I continued my journey on "a lonesome road" into more undiscovered country.

Police Department City and County of Honolulu
OFFENSE REPORT
Investigator A. McDougal
Investigator Reassigned C. A
Beat 13
Cause of Death Unknown
Watch 1 2 3 4
Hour 9:00 pm
Complainant BROWN, John I.
Address Manoa, Oahu
Address Honolulu
where occurred Pier 12, Honolulu
when occurred Date 6-13-42
Date 7-23-42
Reported by BROWN Mrs.
Date 7-23-42
Reported to District Station 13
Report typewritten by A. McDougal
On beat
Phone
Letter
where victim was found. No Signs of a
nd all secondary evidence unclear as t
under suspicion.

Memo
Date Aug. 13
Ms C. called again.
Scared to death about
something! Needs to
meet with you A.S.A.P!
Coming by at 8:00pm

Dark File IV:

When Demons Possess and Souls Torment

Have you ever felt that the events taking place in your life were selected to occur by some unseen power that had a distinct, ultimate purpose in taking you down a certain pathway? If you are a religious person, you may interpret this as "God's Plan" or "predestination" for your life. If you embrace reincarnation as a belief, then you may view the meaningful chain of coincidences that take place in our daily existence as a predetermined cosmic scenario through which we learn lessons in our spiritual development through many incarnations. If you don't think much of these matters and take life basically on a day-to-day basis, you may conclude that the whole roller coaster of living is based on pure and simple "luck." Some of us have it, most of us don't.

To know the patterns that are unfolding in our lives, however, takes many years to discern. It is as if we are on a trek through a dense rain forest. Every day we hack our way through the jungle vines and thick foliage, never totally certain where we are going, but vaguely aware that we are heading somewhere. Occasionally we have setbacks that confuse us, throwing us in new directions. Finally, we reach a high-enough peak so that we can look back on the progress we have thus far made, and we are surprised how clearly the path behind us seems designed to lead us to our present place. It is as if all those blind twists and turns we had to take were meaningfully charted so that we could achieve our ultimate goal.

When I have occasionally been given the insight to look back from the mountain peak, and to prognosticate where the path I've walked as a ghost story collector will finally lead, I sometimes have felt a tiny dread which makes me hesitate to continue the journey—for, although this bewildering love for the supernatural has brought immense attention to a person otherwise wholly ordinary, the pathway has been too often crossed by hints that I am being prepared not for adulation, but confrontation. What is it that I will one day need to confront? I cannot at this point definitively answer that question which I continually pose to myself. But I know one thing—it will be Evil.

My first encounter with this dark force was 21 years ago, in the winter of 1976. In September of that year I had become involved in the political campaign of a young Hawaiian politician who would go on to many years of service in the Hawai'i State Legislature. Through a mutual friend, I had been introduced to this rising political star and his civic philosophy, which aroused my sense of social idealism. So, for many weeks I held signs along the Ala Wai Canal, waving at passing automobiles with the familiar "shaka" sign, going door-to-door to hand out leaflets and to have doors slammed in my face, while vicious dogs chased me out of the yard. I hated every moment of it, but "my man" won.

The best part of the campaign was getting to know the 'ohana or family that had poured out in support for their relative and friend. Although I had entered the campaign as a stranger, I emerged with a host of good friends with whom I would stay in contact over subsequent years. One of those friends was Cathy Kau, an attractive, young Hawaiian woman who had then just awakened to her own ethnic heritage in those vibrant cultural days now called the "Hawaiian Renaissance." A devotee of "Sunday Manoa" and "Olomana," she never missed Kanikapila, the annual Hawaiian music and dance festival at the University of Hawai'i's Andrew Amphitheater. She joined a *hula halau,* studied the Hawaiian language, and devoted her reading time to exploring the history of the Islands. When her cousin announced that he was running for political office, she enthusiastically joined the effort, being a part of my sign-waving team. Once, she was gracious enough to go out with me to a dinner and movie, but I quickly learned that she had too many men attracted to her to feel the need to choose any single one of them as her exclusive boyfriend.

So, I was sorry when the November elections were over because that meant that I would probably no longer have an opportunity to see Cathy. Her phone call on Thanksgiving Day, therefore, came as a complete surprise. She needed someone to talk to, she said, and thought perhaps I would be the perfect person.

"You are still into the supernatural, yeah?" Cathy asked.

"Of course," I assured her.

"Good," she said in her usual upbeat tone. "Then I need your advice. Can we get together tomorrow? Wanna go to the beach?"

We sat at Sans Souci beach at Waikiki for a few hours that Friday, as Cathy explained a very sad situation which had happened to her cousin, whom for the sake of anonymity I will call "Ku'ulei." Born and raised on the island of O'ahu at Kahalu'u, Ku'ulei was the daughter of the youngest and most favorite sister of Cathy's mother. The two women had been so close to one another that they made sure even in their adult lives that they would always stay neighbors. Consequently, Cathy and Ku'ulei, who were exactly the same age, grew up together just as if they had been *hanai* sisters. They were inseparable, spending summers together, joining the same Girl Scout unit, attending the same public schools and graduating in the same class at the University of Hawai'i.

While Cathy had gone on after graduation to immerse herself in her Hawaiian heritage during a period of a state-wide cultural revival, Ku'ulei went in the opposite direction. Being fair-skinned with blue eyes, she always highlighted her brown hair with bleached streaks to emphasize her haole features. On the state census she always listed her ethnic heritage as "Caucasian" after her father and dated only Caucasian men, finally marrying David, an athletic, good-looking haole from a *kama'aina* family on the island of Kaua'i. Ku'ulei rarely ate Hawaiian food, hardly listened to KCCN radio and never, ever put her fingers into three-day-old poi.

Three years after her marriage, Ku'ulei was devoted to her husband and their one-year-old son, Shane, who was born with light-brown hair, blue eyes and white skin. They lived in Lihu'e, Kaua'i, where Ku'ulei's husband was a successful administrator for the county. She became a full-time housewife and mother with more and more time on her hands to become involved with craft projects, community nonprofit organizations and reading. Ku'ulei was an avid reader, who especially enjoyed gothic romances, tales of the occult and books on magic and astrology. As the weeks and months passed in her blissful, loving marriage, she had more and more time to look for the imperfections in her perfect life.

"White magic" was the perfect antidote to her boredom. Although she had been raised a devout Catholic with a dread of Satan, witchcraft in the 1970s had become a fashionable pastime for a generation of young Americans who saw the embodiment of Evil within the Establishment, not alternative forms of religion. Paganism was celebrated, along with drugs, free love and Age of Aquarius spirituality in all forms of music, poetry, prose and counterculture lifestyles. This was the decade of Carlos Castaneda's *The Teachings of Don Juan: The Yaqui Way of Knowledge* which glorified peyote, mysticism and magic. On the island of Kaua'i, an early vanguard of "hippies" out of California had established themselves and were laying the seeds at Hanalei for a "new age," holistic healing revolution which would spiritually transform the Garden Island by the end of the century.

Ku'ulei was at first repulsed by the "hippies" who had moved to Kaua'i. Their rebellion against middle-class standards of dress and behavior grated her upbringing in Kahalu'u. In time, however, her prejudices relaxed, when she discovered that some of these "flower children" were wonderful astrologers and tarot card readers. The little coffee and "paraphernalia" shops that they opened were "funky," and always smelled sweet from the burning incense. Ku'ulei even started to wear patchouli oil perfume, which had become popular among the "long hairs."

Her husband, David, never fully understood his wife's attraction to these unkempt newcomers. As a *kama'aina haole,* there was perhaps a little resentment that this new class of Caucasian only made matters more difficult in a local community increasingly being altered by tourists and what some called the "Californication" of the Islands. He hated the patchouli oil perfume, advised his wife against painting colorful flowers on his son's face for entertainment, and refused to wear the "tie-dye" tee shirt that she had purchased as a matching set for the entire family. The books that she was reading on witchcraft, he now constantly chided her, were trash. On a few occasions, he even took the liberty of throwing away a few of the books which were particularly occult-oriented.

In the ensuing months, Ku'ulei spent an increasing amount of time with one particular "family" in Hanalei that operated a small "paraphernalia" shop. Although they called themselves a "family," there were no blood relatives among its members, only a loose collection of friends and lovers who had once lived in a commune in Northern California. David wasn't certain if Ku'ulei was involved in any of the drugs that the family obviously used, but he protested vigorously on many occasions how she and Shane were embarrassing him in the community. As a county administrator, how did it look when his wife had become so chummy with such strange riffraff? The more her husband attacked her new friends, the more Ku'ulei in her heart defended them.

At first Cathy had received regular phone calls from Ku'ulei, who kept her abreast on the growth of Shane, life in the slow lane and her growing interest in astrology and magic. When the "family" became a part of her life, Ku'ulei called less frequently. Concerned for her very closest cousin, indeed her sister, Cathy decided to visit Kaua'i for a weekend. When she told Ku'ulei about her travel plans, her cousin seemed totally blasé about the visit, even though they had not seen each other for over a year.

A very sullen David picked Cathy up at the Li'hue airport on Saturday morning. When she asked him where were Ku'ulei and Shane, he simply muttered that they would meet her back at the house. Cathy tried to coax more information about Ku'ulei out of David on the short ride to the beautiful, old style manager's home that David had inherited from his family. He was very tight-lipped, but when, they finally parked in the driveway, he briefly confided to her that he was very, very worried about his wife. She had fallen into the wrong crowd, he said. Could Cathy try maybe to put some sense back into her?

Ku'ulei and Shane weren't at the house when Cathy arrived. In fact, she and Shane had not been home for two days, David finally confessed. For the last few weeks, she had been sleeping over at the home of the "hippies" and came back to the house only to do her laundry, take food out of the refrigerator and steal money out of David's wallet. Her eyes were invariably glazed and bloodshot, obviously from smoking *pakalolo*. Shane was dirty, his unchanged diapers always soiled, and his hair unkempt and ridiculously long. As far as Ku'ulei was concerned, he said, she was nothing like the girl that he had married who had been always immaculately groomed and always fashionable in her dress and make-up. Quite simply, he said with disdain, she had become a "hippie."

Cathy was indeed shocked by her cousin's appearance when Ku'ulei casually jumped out of the back of a beaten-up old car that pulled up in front of the house two hours later. The car was being driven by a shirtless, deeply tanned, young, blond-haired man with a straggly beard, which he had appeared to be trying to grow for several months. Snuggled in his arm was a young, local Filipino girl who looked like she was only 14 or 15 years old. Ku'ulei cradled Shane in her arm as she climbed out of the car, leaned back in, and gave a passionate kiss to a dark figure who sat regally stretched out across the back seat, one arm draped leisurely across the seat, the other arm resting in the window. He never even moved one inch forward to acknowledge Ku'ulei's affection, but received her kiss as if he were her master. Cathy could not see him very well, but instantly disliked this middle-aged, darkly sinister man who she could sense had seduced her cousin. After Ku'ulei slammed the back door, the Svengali-figure gave a nod and the car roared off back down the lane to the main road.

Although the changes in Ku'ulei were dramatic, in a short time she and Cathy were able to reconnect and were talking away like those nights when they were at the university, staying up until morning to talk about life. When they were alone in the backyard, Ku'ulei lit a joint of *pakalolo,* which Cathy refused to share. Immediately, Ku'ulei started talking affectionately about her new friend, Ekimmu, who had become her spiritual guide and counselor. He was from eastern Europe, where he had learned all of the ancient arts of "white" magic. Eventually Ekimmu found his way to Kaua'i via Berkeley, California, where he had gathered about him a loving family of fellow "witches and warlocks." They were all so open and free and in tune with the universe, Ku'ulei enthusiastically told Cathy. They weren't confined by the middle-class conventions that made people like David so boring. When Cathy asked if she had been intimate with this Ekimmu, Ku'ulei became very graphic with the descriptions of their lovemaking. She was wholly unashamed of her infidelities, giving Cathy the excuse that David was a slouch in bed.

When Cathy refused to go with Ku'ulei back to Hanalei to meet Ekimmu and his "family," the two cousins separated with a quick hug, as the same old battered car pulled up to the house at a prearranged hour. At David's insistence, Ku'ulei gladly left Shane behind and jumped into the back seat, where the mysterious figure of Ekimmu waited. The couple embraced, as the "family" car drove off with the silhouette of two heads in the back window kissing passionately.

David told Cathy that his mother advised him to divorce Ku'ulei, get custody of Shane, and sever all further connections with her. But he loved his wife, he tearfully told Cathy. How could he abandon her when obviously she was being manipulated by some evil people? He couldn't force her to stay away from them, but he was praying she would come to her senses. Cathy promised to stay in touch, curtailed her plans for a weekend on Kaua'i, and caught the first available flight back to O'ahu.

Two weeks later she received a midnight phone call from Ku'ulei. Her voice was hysterical, as she tried to explain that Ekimmu had taken up with another woman, throwing her out of his bed. She felt totally abandoned. What was she to do? Cathy suggested that she go back to David and Shane. How could I, Ku'ulei said, after what I had done to him? David loved her very much, Cathy advised her, and would happily take her back. He was a very forgiving man. Ku'ulei promised that she would think about it.

When Ku'ulei hanged up, Cathy called David immediately to tell him what had happened. He hadn't seen Ku'ulei in over a week and had no idea where she could be, assuming she was with Ekimmu. Now that she had been thrown out of the "family," there was no telling where she was staying. He promised to call Cathy the minute he heard from Ku'ulei.

The next day, Cathy told her mother and aunt everything about what had happened to Ku'ulei on Kaua'i. They had known that David and Ku'ulei were having problems in their marriage, but they had no idea about Ekimmu, the "white witchcraft" and other problems, including drugs. By that afternoon, the three of them flew to Kaua'i. hopefully to rescue this once-beautiful girl who was sinking so fast into self-destructive behavior. With the help of the police, they tracked her down at the home of a local man who said he had met her the night before, hitchhiking on the road. She had nowhere to go, she said, so he brought her back to his place, where they had spent the night together. Ku'ulei was half-naked in his bed, stoned on grass and unwillingly to go home to David. It was a terrible scene—with her mother screaming and calling her nasty names, as her daughter simply laughed. Finally, Ku'ulei had to be forcibly restrained and brought back to her Li'hue home, where a very apprehensive David tried to show his wife that she was indeed welcome.

Ku'ulei's mother decided to stay with her daughter to help her reclaim her life. She made sure that Ku'ulei stayed away from drugs and alcohol, helped her take care of Shane, and continually counseled her on her behavior. The two women went to Mass at the Li'hue Catholic church every day where Ku'ulei made confessions for her sins. Although she would secretly sometimes try to call Ekimmu, who always refused to talk with her, she seemed to come back slowly to her senses. In fact, her mother was very relieved when Ku'ulei made a new friend in Li'hue, an older Hawaiian woman who was another frequent worshipper at the church. In time this woman encouraged Ku'ulei to attend a small Hawaiian mystical church on the island which would satisfy her need not only for religion, but supernatural faith. The older Hawaiian woman was very eclectic in her religious worship, being open to all aspects of spirit and the otherworld.

Ku'ulei now entered a new phase of her life as she discovered her Hawaiian heritage, became very religious and denounced the "white" magic that she had practiced as "satanic." All of her books on the occult and magic, David was pleased to see, were burned in the backyard. Although the affection they had once felt for one another had been irretrievably lost, at least they now respected one another. Ku'ulei's mother returned finally to

O'ahu, secure that her daughter was walking on the right path.

None of them, least of all Cathy, expected the explosion which would shatter all of their lives that week of Thanksgiving 1976. David later explained that Ku'ulei had become convinced that Ekimmu, who she now believed was the Devil Incarnate, was trying to pray her to death. At night she would wake up horrified that she was being sexually aroused as she dreamt of a beast penetrating her body and soul. At the advice of a deaconess in the mystical Hawaiian church, she had performed a *pi kai* or ceremonial sprinkling of salt water about the four corners of her bedroom. When this failed to stop the sexual assaults in her dreams, Ku'ulei was then advised to sprinkle her *mimi* or urine in the four corners of the house. *Mimi* was believed to contain an evil supernatural power which would repel any other evil power approaching the home.

Finally, on the Tuesday afternoon before Thanksgiving Day, David returned home to find Ku'ulei sitting alone, sullen, in the bedroom. Shane was crying, neglected and hungry, in his playpen. When he tried to talk to her, she refused to answer. Going back into the kitchen to prepare a little food for Shane, David suddenly heard a wild scream coming from the bedroom. When he ran back to see what was wrong with Ku'ulei, he saw that she was standing in the middle of the bed, ripping her clothes off and screaming that her body was on fire. Then a bizarre look appeared in her eyes as she stood naked on the bed, muttering in a low, growling manly voice that she was Kuwahailo, or "Ku-maggot-mouthed," one of the forms of an ancient god of Hawai'i.

Her body literally seemed to fly across the room as she bounced off the bed, hands outstretched as she grabbed David by the throat, the manly voice within her now declaring that he hated *haole,* all *haole* and she was going to kill him and the baby. The hands about his neck seemed of superhuman strength as he felt the wind cut off in his throat, his head burning in fear and pain as he stumbled back into the hallway, slamming into the wall. With all of his might, he struck Ku'ulei on the side of her head, throwing her to the floor. With a single leap, she rose from the floor and flew into the kitchen, grabbing one of the butcher knives from a wall rack. Again, that horrible voice inside her, spewing abominable filth, screamed that the *haole* will all die. She now ran to the playpen where Shane was screeching, watching his demonic mother rush towards him, blade in hand, planning to plunge the weapon into the heart of her own infant.

Fortunately, David was able to grab her from behind and force her to the floor where he pinned her with his body. Beneath him, he heard

Kuwahailo promise to put maggots into David's body, to eat his flesh and rip out the heart of his white-skinned son. Finally, his wife's body relaxed as she let out a long deep sigh, as if expelling some spirit from within. Ku'ulei's naked flesh was now trembling in terror as David took her back to her room, called the ambulance, and had her taken to Wilcox Memorial Hospital.

The doctors, Cathy told me as she completed her story that morning at Sans Souci Beach, have concluded that Ku'ulei is suffering from a mild form of schizophrenia, perhaps exacerbated by her recent adultery, which had caused deep anxieties of guilt and shame. To relieve her guilt, she has tried to eliminate the source of her shame—her husband and son, whom she wronged. They suggested a long stay at the clinic and extensive psychiatric counseling.

The old Hawaiian woman advised David that his wife had suffered from a false *akua noho* or god possession. A person possessed by a god, she explained, was not *pupule* or insane, but was filled with divine *mana* or supernatural power. This may be *noho ia*, a wild possession which could reach a state of madness. The possession, she also suggested, may have been inflicted upon her by someone else, possibly the strange magician with whom she had had the affair. However, this type of spirit possession was temporary, she went on to reassure David. His wife would soon be herself if a certain type of exorcism were to be performed. At this point, however, David was relying more on the advice of doctors than what he believed to be the hocus-pocus of the old woman.

Cathy wanted to know what I thought about the bizarre series of events that led her cousin to almost kill her husband and son in a rage against *haole*. Was demonic possession a true supernatural phenomena as suggested just a couple of years before in the book and film by William Blatty, *The Exorcist* or was the condition entirely psychological? Should we commit her to the care of the psychiatrists, Cathy wanted to know, or follow the advice of the old Hawaiian woman and perform an exorcism that would return Ku'ulei to "normal"?

My experience with demonic possession at that time was entirely limited to what I had read in books. The classic work on the subject had been published in 1921 by a German philosopher named Traugott K. Oesterreich. *Possession and Exorcism* was a very complete work that examined not only the historical cases surrounding demonic possession, but studied possession in the Old and New Testament, stressing the role of Jesus Christ as an exorcist. Oesterreich concluded that the universality of the possession experience, the common impression of horror that it produces, and a feeling of something sinister that emerges from within the victim strongly suggested a "parapsychic" phenomena that demanded further research. In other words, demonic possession as commonly found in the cultures of all of Hawai'i's people from Polynesia, to Asia and Europe, is rooted not simply in the psychological, but in the paranormal.

Was Ku'ulei actually one of these victims of possession? According to Oesterreich, several conditions determined a true demonic possession. The first characteristic is a changed physiognomy. The face and body of the possessed dramatically transform during the possession, sometimes even assuming the form of a deceased person who is allegedly the possessing spirit. The second characteristic is an altered voice within the possessed person. In effect, the voice of the dead, male or female, can be heard speaking from the victim. Thirdly, the voice within the possessed person assumes a new identity, different and distinct from the old ego that it has replaced. This new personality is also coarse, filthy and vile, its words and thoughts opposed to all the fundamental tenets of ethics and religion. Based upon this criteria and the description of events as relayed by Cathy, the possession of Ku'ulei seemed very, very plausible. However, I reminded her, I was. of course, not at the scene of the possession to see for myself that these criteria had all been met. I was relying entirely on hearsay.

"By the way, Cathy," I asked her, "do you know what Ekimmu means?"

"It must be some European name, yeah?"

"It is Assyrian," I told her, remembering the name from my study of demonic possession. "It refers to an evil ghost of one who was denied entrance to the otherworld and is therefore doomed to walk this world forever. It was a murderous, demonic being."

In the years after that morning spent talking about sinister devils on a beautiful Waikiki beach, there would be a few other cases I would include in *The Secret Obake Casebook* where the question of demonic possession would rear its horned, slimy head. Personally, I avoid this kind of supernatural tale like the plague; I flee from its approach like a man desperate to find a cellar at the sound of a nearing tornado. But every once in a while, despite all the best laid plans of mice and men, the demons find their way into the darkest corners of my cabinet.

The Woman With the Long, Sexy, Black Hair Casebook Entry #3335

Date of Entry: November 9, 1994

Supernatural Category: Demonic Possession/Incubus/Exorcism

"*Do you believe* in sexual possession, Dr. Grant?"

I puzzled over the inquiry for several minutes, trying to figure out if it was a trick question. Although I had often thought about being possessed sexually, I couldn't say that I necessarily believed in it. Certainly not in my lifetime, but I was very open-minded.

"What do you mean, Mike?"

"Do you believe that a ghost can get into somebody and then use their body for sex?"

Mike Maglasang was a big, 26-year-old Filipino-American security guard at the International Market Place in Waikiki where once a week I perform ghost storytelling at the Waikiki Heritage Theater. The show, which is attended almost exclusively by local people, is called "The Ghosts of Hawai'i." Since at the end of the program we often turn the lights down so that the audience can hopefully experience a supernatural encounter with the ghost that actually does haunt the theater, it is not uncommon to hear screams and other frantic yells emanating from the building. As a security officer, it is of course his job to investigate disturbances at the Market Place. Therefore, one night in response to the yelling, he came over to "check us out." Intrigued with Hawai'i's "chicken skin" tales, he started hanging out at the theater on the nights of the shows and even bought a ticket to attend.

So, when he asked me about sexual possession one afternoon as I was arriving with the staff to prepare the theater for the performance, I promised him that I would first look it up in my handy The Encyclopedia of Ghosts and Spirits by Rosemary Ellen Guiley. Under the heading "Demons," Guiley does mention the famous incubus and succubus of medieval Europe which she defines as a similar hellish monster that separately attacks men and women: "A succubus, or demon masquerading as a voluptuous woman, molested men, while the incubus, a demon masquerading as a man, molested women." She notes a famous 1986 case involving a family named Smurl that lived in a haunted house in West Pittston, Pennsylvania. One night the husband claimed that a beautiful young woman crawled into bed with him. As she began to rape him, she turned into a scaly succubus with green gums and red burning eyes. The wife was similarly raped on another night by an incubus. The full story of the Smurl haunting was described by Robert Curran in *The Haunted: One Family's Nightmare.*

There have been a few firsthand accounts which I have collected involving the disturbing thought of having sex with a ghost. In most cases, the living person who is seduced or raped by the entity is terrified and defiled by the experience, in a few cases they actually enjoy the liaison with the spirit. Occasionally the lovemaking between a young couple has been known to attract malevolent spirits who seem drawn to robust sexual activity.

For example, a young man told me how, after escorting his girlfriend on one of my walking tours of downtown Honolulu, he returned with her to his home in Nu'uanu Valley. In fact, he said, he lived not far from the infamous Morgan's Corner on Nu'uanu Pali Drive. Since his girlfriend was only visiting from Dallas, Texas, and was scheduled to go home the next day, their last night together was particularly passionate. They fell asleep at about 2:00 AM when suddenly he was awakened by the yells of his girlfriend. He opened his eyes just in time to see the horror that had made her scream.

She claimed that she was sound asleep, when she felt her boyfriend's leg rub up against her naked body. He snuggled up against her, placing his lips upon your neck. His hands moved passionately across her breasts and then thighs, as she aroused herself for what she thought would be another session of lovemaking. When she opened her eyes, she saw that her lover wasn't her boyfriend. Laying between the two of them was a dark shadowy cloud that stretched the full length of the bed. The cloud was in the crude, amorphous form suggesting a human male who was now pressing her back down into the bed and preparing to mount her. Her wild screams woke up her boyfriend, who claimed that he saw this shapeless entity just before it vanished.

The girlfriend's near-assault wasn't the last incident with this invading spirit that he believes he brought home from my walking tour. The entity now sleeps with him at night. Sometimes he awakens to see this black mist floating over him and then he feels the pressing, choking sensation as his body is paralyzed. On another occasion, his mother walked by his room one early morning and saw the dark cloud floating over him as he lay motionless in his bed. It was as if the "thing" was about to rape him.

In ancient Hawai'i, it was not uncommon that a man or woman could have a dream or spirit lover who came to their bed at night. These erotic spirits were called *kane o ka po* or *wahine o ka po*, man or woman of the night. In some cases, I have heard stories of how the *kane o ka po,* sometimes described as a dark shadowy figure, would emerge from the sea to sleep with his human lover who would later become pregnant. A child born of this union would be considered different or *'e'epa,* a remarkable person of miraculous powers. One woman who frequently shared her affections with a *kane o ka po* was reported by Mary Pukui in *The Polynesian Family System of Ka'u* as becoming listless with no appetite. She desired only to sleep so that she could be with her dream lover. In time, the right side of her body where the spirit laid at night, became slimy like a fish. Only an exorcism by the woman's husband restored her to health.

When I finally saw Mike a couple of weeks later, I presented him with a few copies of the materials that I found which referred to "sexual possession." None of them, I noted, included stories of spirits inside the body—whether incubus, succubus, *kane o ka po* or *wahine o ka po*, the spirit made love to the exterior of the body.

Of course, I added, if you review the history of demonic-possessed women during the sixteenth and seventeenth centuries, many of them were sexually repressed nuns and young women who, during the satanic episode, became sexually aggressive or claimed that their bodies were being used by the Devil. During the exorcisms, usually conducted by male priests, sexual sadomasochistic behaviors on the part of the exorcist were directed toward the women who sometimes died during their "cure." Witches, according to European tradition, regularly had sexual relations with demons that sucked their blood at a place on the flesh called a "witch's tit." These blemishes were the sign that someone had been "familiar" with spirits.

I had hoped that my research, insufficient as it had been, would satisfy Mike's curiosity about sexual possession. I jokingly asked him if it was a problem for him. Was a woman sexually possessing him at night?

"Nah, not me, Doc," he said, "my mother-in-law."

"Your mother-in-law then is possessed sexually by a ghost?"

"That's what her *kahuna* said. He said she got inside her the ghost of a man. Weird, yeah? So I figured I'd ask you."

I immediately asked Mike if he would mind telling me the story. This was a unique type of supernatural occurrence, and I wanted to record it for my *Obake Files*. However, as the story unfolded, I realized that this was not a story to be published with the other hauntings of the Islands. There was something strangely sinister about this story that qualified it for the secret casebook.

Mike's mother-in-law, Aurora Los Banos, was an immigrant from the Republic of the Philippines who moved to Hawai'i in the late 1960s, when the U.S. immigration laws had been rewritten to allow for the re-uniting of families. A great many immigrants from the Philippines moved to the Islands at that time to join relatives who had moved to Hawai'i in the late 1940s or before World War II. Since tourism was just beginning to boom with the advent of statehood and jet passenger airlines, service industry jobs in housekeeping and maintenance were readily available to these new Asian immigrants.

Aurora worked many years for the Outrigger hotel chain in Waikiki, moving from one hotel property to another every few years as determined by management. An excellent worker with an outstanding record of performance and hardly ever missing a workday, Aurora was frequently cited by her supervisor as "Employee of the Month" and enjoyed the respect and goodwill of everyone in the Outrigger chain. In addition, Aurora was a lovely woman with a wonderful personality who was always cheerful to the guests, sharing with them a sincere *"aloha."* Although she didn't have daily direct contact with guests, she always saw her primary role as extending hospitality with a bright smile to anyone she met in the hotel.

One of the guests who used to return regularly to the particular hotel that Aurora was working at in the 1990s was a Canadian "snowbird" who spent summers at home in British Columbia, but who lived for three months out of the year at the Outrigger. Bob Swinton was a widower about 80 years old who was as spry as any man half his age. Every year he would stay in a unit that was rented out on a monthly basis by the hotel as an apartment. All day long he would be strolling along the beach, getting a deep brown tan, or ballroom dancing at the Waikiki Community Center, which had programs for senior citizens. He always seemed to have a new girlfriend on his arm, Aurora noted, when he was seen lounging at the Outrigger pool.

As nice as she was to everyone, Aurora did hold back just a bit whenever seeing or talking to Swinton. In her own words, he was a "dirty old man" who used to make lewd remarks whenever she would clean his apartment. On some days he purposely waited for her to do the vacuuming just so he could follow her around, touching her in familiar places and making lewd jokes about them together. At first she tolerated it because he was a guest. But then she complained to her supervisors, who moved her off

Swinton's floor. Of course that didn't really stop him from harassing her. He'd track her down to whatever floor she was on to make his filthy comments.

Aurora found his lewdness especially repulsive because, not only was she a devout Catholic, but she had been a widow for several years and was uncomfortable around sexually aggressive men. When she saw him coming down the hall, her "*aloha*" quickly vanished, giving him as cold a shoulder as she could muster. She threw in a few stink eyes, as well. Nothing worked. The more she tried to rebuff him, the more ardent his attentions became. When one day she finally asked him why he didn't just leave her alone, he said that he had made love to a woman of almost every nationality in the world but one—a Filipino. He wanted her to be his first. The offer repulsed her, as she felt tingles of disgust crawl up her flesh.

Aurora endured Mr. Swinton for three years of "snowbird" visits when, during his fourth year, he dropped dead one afternoon at the pool. A heart attack, the manager told Aurora, had been the cause of death. Bob Swinton had no wife or children, but he had listed a nephew on the "notify in case of an accident" line on his rental form. Since the nephew could not be located for several days, the hotel decided to pack up Swinton's things, while the corpse was kept by the coroner's department. Aurora had been given the assignment to clean Swinton's room, packing all his belongings, which she brought to the manager's office.

She first felt something unusual in the closet, where she was pulling out his clothes and folding them into a suitcase. As she told her son-in-law later, a feeling was at her shoulder that a presence was looking at her. When she turned, there was no one there, but again, when she stepped into the closet, the uneasy feeling returned. It was as if someone was following her around the room, leering at her. Of course, it could have been her imagination, since Mr. Swinton had been a lecherous old bastard who in life had harassed her. Maybe she was just remembering his disgusting habits and projected them into the room as if he was invisibly present.

It was about 10:00 PM when she finally finished cleaning up his unit and carting everything down to the manager's office. She only had to finish cleaning the bathroom and then the apartment would be ready for occupancy. Aurora was scrubbing the sink, when she had the distinct feeling that something had brushed the back of her right calf. She looked down, almost expecting to see a dog or cat walking into the bathroom. There was nothing there. A moment later, again something brushed up against her leg. Again, there was nothing there. Hurrying to finish the job, she wiped the mirror on the wall and noticed in the reflection the doorway behind her. For a brief moment it seemed as if someone—a tall, elderly haole—had just walked past the bathroom door. The vision was brief, although the figure of the man was clearly Bob Swinton.

Aurora didn't wait to put her cleaning implements back in her cart, to neatly fold the end of the toilet paper roll, or give the room one last, quick inspection. She was screaming down the hallway through the hotel, hitting the door button to the elevator and praying whatever had walked by that door didn't follow her out of the room. In seconds she was in the elevator, going down to the basement laundry area, where she would tell anyone who cared to listen about her strange encounter in the room of the dead man.

In the Philippines, the spirits of the dead are sometimes feared to be aswang or vampire witches who can bring illness or even death to the living. When she got home that evening, Aurora made secret precautions against these demons so as to protect her Waipahu apartment. Early the next morning, she went to the Catholic church near her home to attend Mass, give confession and receiving blessings. She talked with her priest about the vision of the dead man walking through the hotel room and together they prayed for her protection. Since the priest was not Filipino, she did not mention the *aswang*.

Two days later, Aurora awoke with severe pains in the joints of her fingers. She could hardly open the twist-top of the detergent jar at work as a tiny explosion of needles pricked her joints and skin from within. The next day her knees and elbows were similarly afflicted until, by the end of the week, the painful sensations were crippling every joint and bone in her body.

Usually Aurora was so healthy that she hadn't missed a day of work in 10 years. Her supervisor was therefore extremely concerned when she called in one morning to say that she had to go to the doctor for an examination. The physician ran a few tests, talked to Aurora at length about the nature of the pain and then suggested to her that she may have the first stages of arthritis. He prescribed some medicine, which she faithfully took, but the pain never subsided. As a month passed, the arthritis became more intense.

Finally, one of Aurora's girlfriends at work suggested that, if the pain started after she saw that ghost, then maybe she should go to a Hawaiian *kahuna*. There was a very good man whom she recommended who lived in Kalihi Valley, not far from the Kamehameha IV housing. Since Aurora believed she was a visitor here in the Islands, and the Hawaiians were the hosts, then maybe it would be a good idea to have a Hawaiian blessing. Her friend made a call, and, after work, Aurora took the bus to Kalihi, where she found the priest's house without trouble.

The *kahuna* was a quiet old gentleman who listened silently to Aurora briefly describe the ghost that she had seen at the Outrigger hotel and the pain she was now suffering. He sat in an old, stuffed chair that over the years curved naturally to his body, which was tall and lean. His intense gaze into Aurora's eyes made her feel a little uncomfortable, as if he could look through her pupils into her soul.

"Did this man want you sexually?"

He spoke these words so clearly and distinctly, Aurora felt a little uncomfortable to answer. She had left that part of the story out of her little hotel encounter.

"Yes, he did."

"I know that. You see, in life he wanted you, but he could not have you. You are a pure woman. In death, he is not bound to his body any longer. When you went into his room to touch his clothing, his spirit was able to enter into you. What he couldn't have in life, he now has in death. He is inside your body, touching you from the inside. Every time his spirit hands rub your flesh, it causes the pain."

The tingling which Aurora had been feeling in her joints and flesh now took on a horrific new meaning as she imagined Bob Swinton's ghost inside her body even now, touching her from the inside. At least when he was alive, she could run away or brush his hand off. Now there was no way that she could keep him from touching even her most private parts! Her whole body began to tremble from a nightmarish thought that she couldn't erase from her mind!

"Get him out of me! Get him out of me!" she screamed hysterically, feeling his hands inside her flesh, running its fingers down her thigh to her calves.

"I can pray for you and perhaps that will help. But this man you said was *haole* and you are Filipino. I don't know how strong my prayers will be since neither of you are Hawaiian."

That evening Aurora called everyone she knew for the name of a priest who would be able to exorcise the spirit having sex with her from the inside.

"Has she had the ritual?" I asked Mike.

"Not yet. She got the name of a Filipino woman who is also some kind of massage healer. I don't know anything about her except that she can drive the devil and *aswang* out of the living. Hey, Doc, if my mother-in-law doesn't mind, you wanna watch?"

Mike called Aurora and explained to her who I was and what my interest would be in observing the ritual. She was reluctant to have a complete stranger at the ceremony, which was to be conducted on Sunday morning in Aurora's apartment. But, since nearly the whole family was going to be in attendance, why turn away one more? I promised to be as unobtrusive as possible.

Sunday morning after Mass, I met Mike at the Waipahu High School parking lot so that he could direct me to Aurora's apartment building. When I arrived, she had been preparing a huge feast for the priestess, her family members, Mike and his ghost storytelling friend. Aurora was very friendly to me, but you could see that she was a bit uncomfortable with my presence at the blessing. I had heard many years before that in the Philippines a person who loves to tell ghost stories is sometimes suspected of being themselves a vampire *aswang*. I wondered if she had begun to doubt my soul and my interest at watching this kind of exorcism.

The massaging priestess arrived at exactly 12:00 PM to first partake in the meal, comprised of all types of Filipino delicacies, including *lumpia,* pork *adobo,* and a seaweed salad called pokpoklo. She was very quiet and spoke only in the Filipino language of Tagalog, refusing to use English. When she was finished with her meal, she asked Aurora to go with her into the bedroom where the exorcism would take place. I could see that Aurora was visibly in pain from the arthritis, which had become so intense in her knees that she hobbled a bit when she walked.

Mike, his wife and I were starting to join them in the bedroom, when the Filipino priestess said something to Aurora in her language, pointing at the three of us, which was obviously a complaint about so many witnesses. This ceremony was to be performed without an audience. Aurora apologized and asked if we could all sit in the living room until the ceremony was over. However, before they shut the door, I could see that the priestess had several objects that she brought out of a shopping bag. There were some ritualistic candles in the bag, which she placed on a dresser. She also brought out a small bottle of water, which she carefully placed next to the candles. For some intuitive reason, I assumed the bottle was filled with Holy Water.

The priestess uncapped the bottle and then told Aurora to wash her neck with the water. Just as she began to rub the Holy Water onto her body, the priestess walked over to the door and slammed it shut in our faces.

In a few minutes we could hear the woman praying, but she spoke too fast for Mike or his wife to understand anything that she was saying. Then we heard a loud slapping sound, like someone was striking the flesh with a hand. We probably would have imagined all kinds of things happening in the room, when the door opened about six inches, giving all of us a perfect view into the room. Evidently, when the door slammed, it hadn't properly latched so it had slowly swung back open.

The priestess was so concentrated on the ritual that she hadn't noticed her little audience. She was vigorously slapping Aurora's neck with her open hand as the subject of the exorcism was standing there in dire pain, restraining any screams as her neck became a brilliant red from the stings of flesh-on-flesh. Just when it seemed that the slapping was becoming a torture, the priestess stopped and suddenly grabbed Aurora by the throat with one hand as if to choke her to death. She finally massaged a fleshy piece of Aurora's neck and began to stretch it out from the neck further than what seemed humanly possible, or tolerable. Aurora made no sound during all of this abuse, having been told that her screams or whimpering would ruin the exorcism.

I almost felt guilty watching this strange ritual, but, before I could avert my eyes, the truly horrific aspect of the exorcism commenced. All three of us were fully mesmerized at this point when the priestess seemed to identify a single black hair that was protruding from Aurora's neck. I hadn't noticed the hair on the neck when I first met her, a fact confirmed by Mike, who had known his mother-in-law for three years. Never had he ever seen a single black strand of hair about one or two inches on her neck. Her skin was normally very taut, smooth and hairless.

The single strand of black hair was being held by the priestess in her two fingers as she slowly begin to pull upon it. As we watched from a safe distance in the other room, the hair pulled out longer, and longer, and longer, until the hair in Aurora's neck was at least four feet long! When the hair was extracted, she placed it in a large, empty mayonnaise jar, which had been brought by the priestess for this exact purpose. Then she incredibly reached back to the neck, massaging Aurora again, as another single strand of hair was identified and pulled out until it, too, was about four feet long. This hair was also placed in the jar, as the priestess began the process again, and again, and again, until the jar was filled to the brim with long, black oily hairs extracted from the neck of Aurora.

Since neither woman had noticed Mike, his wife and me at the door, when the last hair was pulled out, we all quickly went outside to the porch to make sure the priestess wouldn't be angry that her ceremony had been observed. All of us agreed that it was truly the most extraordinary sight we had ever seen. If it had been sleight of hand in a fashion such as famous healers around the world have operated on the body using only their hands, then it was an incredible magician's act that would definitely stump David Copperfield or Amazing Randi. Where in the hell that damn hair came from, to this day I have no idea.

The priestess put the lid back on the mayonnaise jar and handed the evil container to Aurora. By then we all gathered back in the living room, the jar sitting on the coffee table. According to Mike's crude translation, the priestess explained to Aurora that the hair was the body of the man who had been sexually assaulting her. She had pulled the spirit out and now confined him in the jar. Tonight, at midnight, Aurora was to throw the hair into a fire until it completely burned. Before I left that afternoon, I took one last, long look at that jar of oily, black hair and felt slightly nauseated not only by its sight, but by what it represented. The rape of a woman or a man by the living monsters who walk among us epitomizes a vulgar evil that takes on new horror when the beast can step back from the grave.

About three weeks later, I saw Mike at the International Market Place. He stopped me briefly to let me know that his mother-in-law's arthritis has now nearly vanished! She was in perfect health and felt absolutely no pain! She was back at work full time at the Outrigger hotel. Congratulating him on the good news, I then turned my attention to the little mayonnaise jar I recalled with disgust.

"Oh, Mike," I matter-of-factly asked, "what happened to the hair? Your mom burned it, right?"

"That's the weird thing, Doc," he said with his own twitch of revulsion. "She still got 'em. I told her, Mom, throw that thing in the fire! Didn't the priestess tell you to burn 'em? But she told me that her best friend is on the mainland and isn't coming home for a few more weeks. She gotta show that hair to her or she'd never believe it! She has to have the proof, yeah?"

As far as I know, that woman still owns that damn long, black, sexy hair in an old jar in her living room, waiting to be burned and that raping demon to be sent back to Hell.

Inu-gami Redux
Casebook Entry [No number given]

Date of Entry:
May 30, 1996

Supernatural Category:
Uncatalogued

Every once in a while an event takes place in your life that upon first reflection seems out of the ordinary, or, more precisely, supernatural. Yet, in the weeks and months that follow, in retrospect you begin to doubt your memory of what had occurred, even rationalizing it as possibly a psychological phenomenon that has nothing to do with intruding spirits. One year later, you have convinced yourself that the demons that you once believed tried to destroy your life are, in reality, faces of your own darker nature, which as human beings we have learned to repress. The incident is at that point left unregistered and uncatalogued by the ghosthunter who realizes that the mysteries of violent human behavior cannot always be blamed on devils.

Therefore, what happened between myself and a "client" commencing in January 1996 may not be a ghost story at all. It may have been simply an unfortunate incident that revealed a shocking deeper truth about what makes a person "snap." The casebook for this incident is therefore a collection of intermittent diary entries which over time illustrates the progressive decline of the personality of a human being put under tremendous pressure until, through his susceptibility to auto-suggestion, he may have conjured up a most fearful demon, its origin unknown.

Thursday, January 4, 1996—3:30 PM

When I returned to my Mo'ili'ili office this afternoon, there was a message taped to my computer screen indicating that at 9:50 AM a Chieko Park had called for me. The note checked two boxes—"PLEASE CALL BACK" and "URGENT." A few minutes later I dialed the phone number which had a "483" prefix, indicating a Pearl City residence. The call was answered by a cheerful female voice who put me on hold when I asked for "Chieko."

When Chieko came on the line, her voice was pleasant, but far more serious.

"Do you know anything about the Pearl Vista Condominiums?" she asked.

"Sure, it is one of the most haunted high-rises in Hawai'i. Why?"

"Oh my God, that's where I live. Why is it haunted?"

I told Chieko in as calm a voice as I could that this condominium project had been delayed due to the discovery of a massive Hawaiian graveyard on the grounds during construction. Since it was opened in the 1980s, I had heard many stories about the building and promised, if she wished, to compile some of my notes so that she could see the range of supernatural events taking place at this site.

Chieko went on to explain to me that she had been quite frightened in the last month by a series of strange events that had happened only to her, not her roommate. They had waited nearly nine months on a waiting list to finally be able to lease for two years their two-bedroom condo on the 30th floor of the building. In the first week after moving in, she had begun to hear knocking on the wall behind her head when she slept at night. At first she thought it was her roommate kicking the wall when she slept at night. So one morning she very tactfully asked why she was knocking on the wall at night. The roommate denied kicking the wall and even had Chieko go into her bedroom while she knocked on the wall in her bedroom with all of her might. The wall between the two rooms was so solid and thick, that you couldn't hear the knocking. That meant whatever was rapping on the wall behind Chieko's head was actually in the wall.

Some nights her CD storage tower would suddenly rattle so strongly that the CDs would literally fly out into the room. On the peripheral of her vision, she claims to see people moving about her bedroom. One evening, sitting up late in bed reading a magazine, she turned off her nightstand lamp to go to sleep. A few minutes later she awoke to a loud "click" in the room. The lamp had been turned back on although Chieko was absolutely alone in the room!

"There have been a few other things that have happened in the last few days," she concluded. "I'd rather tell them to you privately, face to face, if you don't mind. Could we have lunch together, or something?"

I have made arrangements to meet Chieko Park at the C's Cafe on University Avenue, not far from our offices at 12:00 PM tomorrow. Great! Fantastic lead with solid stories. This could lead to possible contact with spirits if she is willing to let us bring in professional psychics!

Notes on Pearl Vista Condominium Haunting Notes (Compiled from various files)

The Pearl Vista Condominium is built on a smallpox burial site uncovered during construction. In 1853 the smallpox epidemic, which killed over 5,000 Hawaiians in Honolulu, could not be contained, raging to other sections of O'ahu and to other islands. The population of native people living at what was later to be called by Benjamin Dillingham's O'ahu Railway and Land Co. "Pearl City" ("Dillinghampton" and "Benville" had also been considered as possible names for this train depot town) were stricken with the terrible disease, their bodies found dead on the beaches where they had tried to "cool" off by laying in the surf. The corpses were greatly feared as a source of contamination, so prisoners from O'ahu Prison had been ordered to gather up the bodies and bury them in huge pits. These unmarked mass graves remained untouched for a century, until the massive residential development of O'ahu in the 1970s and 1980s began uncovering these gruesome and melancholy sites of bodies stacked like lumber.

The Pearl Vista evidently was located directly on one of these smallpox burial sites. Although the bodies had been removed to a nearby graveyard, they were unceremoniously "thrown" into their new mass grave. A kahu for the graveyard had once told me she was furious when she saw the way those bodies had been handled. She came to the graveyard one day to find the workers (who were an imported crew from the mainland, since no local company wanted the job of corpse removal) literally tossing the corpses into the graves from the back of a truck where they had been piled. She warned the men to treat her kupuna or elders with respect. She also told me with sadness that three of those men later died during the construction of the condominium, falling to their deaths in industrial accidents.

Since the building had been occupied, I have collected many firsthand accounts of seeing ghosts in various apartments. A woman claimed that one night as she entered the elevator on the 20th floor to go down to the lobby, she joined three Hawaiians—two men and a woman—standing inside very stoically. No expressions of any kind were upon their faces; their arms hung motionless at their sides. They had evidently gotten into the elevator at a higher floor, but hadn't yet pushed any of the buttons. She pressed the lobby level button and, curious, glanced sideways at her three companions. It was only then she really noticed that none of these three people had any feet! They vanished at their kneecaps! Fortunately, she was able to leap off the elevator before the doors fully closed, but not before letting out a bloodcurdling scream.

Another couple told me how shadows of different-sized human beings moved on the wall in their unit, although they convinced themselves that these unusual shapes were caused by automobile headlights passing the building on the freeway next door. They kept telling themselves that until the night the woman was brushing her teeth at the bathroom mirror. Bending over to rinse her mouth, she rose up to see in the mirror an old Hawaiian woman in a mud-caked dress standing directly behind her. The figure, whose muddy hair was dripping wet, was smiling broadly with a toothless grin at the horrified woman. When she turned, the old woman vanished. The couple moved immediately from the Pearl Vista.

On another occasion a resident of the condominium told me how he had been awakened by security guards in the middle of the night to come down to the basement parking lot. He had forgotten to turn off the headlights of his automobile and, to protect his battery, security had made the early morning call. Yawning as he got into the elevator to go down to the basement, he was surprised to see several other tenants going to the parking lot at 2:00 AM. Mysteriously, the headlights on all of their automobiles had simultaneously turned on, security said, at precisely the same moment!

One former occupant, now living on the mainland and communicating with me through the cyberspace Compuserve Hawai'i Forum, indicated that the only time in his life he had ever experienced *kanashibari* or the "tie-down" choking ghost was when he lived in the Pearl Vista Condominium. Several times he awoke to feel something choking him, pressing him to the bed. He was unable to move or scream, but the pressure finally vanished. Since he moved, the *kanashibari* experiences have never returned. Numerous cases of an outbreak of mental illness while living in the building have been told to me, and the rate of suicidal jumpers is among the highest for any residential building.

The hauntings of the Pearl Vista building continue into 1997. Recently I was informed by an occupant of the 26th floor that he awoke to the sound of a female voice calling his name from outside his bedroom window. Over and over she called out "Thomas," while knocking on the outside glass. He was too terrified to see who it could be calling him, because the other side of the window was a direct drop of 26 stories! The entity was floating outside his apartment!

Friday, January 5, 1996—6:00 PM

Today has been a real shocker. I am not certain that I am at all ready to deal with the problems of the so-called "Chieko Park." I feel that I've been perhaps a little deceived, although I do believe that she is sincere. It is only that I have put all these things very far behind me, and I am greatly reluctant to dredge up the past for what seems to be someone else's troubles. I have enough of my own paranoid crap to deal with to be in a position to take on the load of this woman's anxiety.

When I arrived at C's Cafe, looking forward to the ginger chicken plate lunch that I invariably order to the point that the owner, Sylvia, doesn't even bother any longer to ask what I want, I found Chieko Park sitting alone at a table by the window. I suspected it was her because, first, she was the only woman sitting alone, and, second, she was wearing dark glasses as if she was hiding her identity or embarrassed to fully reveal herself to me. Nervously smoking a cigarette from which she took quick, frequent puffs as if it were a new habit, she appeared to be about 30 or 35 years old. Evidently she worked at some professional capacity, since she was very smartly dressed in an executive suit accentuated by a brightly colored scarf tied stylishly on one side of her neck. Her leather appointment book, which sat on the table in front of her, appeared to be the top of the line from Pocketbook Man at the Ala Moana Shopping Center. While the supernatural knows no boundary of class, race or educational background, I was a bit surprised that someone so obviously from a business-oriented material world would be so drawn to the immaterial world of spirits, ghosts and haunted real estate.

During the routine "protocol" of first meetings, I noted that Chieko Park seemed very familiar to me. Naturally I assumed that she had perhaps been in one of my classes when I was an instructor at the University of Hawai'i, or perhaps Kapi'olani Community College. I couldn't see her eyes behind her dark glasses, but the features of her expertly made-up face indicated that this was someone who had taken many classes in color coordination. The only thing that perhaps detracted from her picture perfect presentation of self were her fingers. I noticed that when she held her hand up to take a drag on her cigarette, the tips of her fingers were unattractively scarred as if she had a skin disorder. It was a curious anomaly to an otherwise obviously confident businesswoman.

After ordering our lunch, Chieko wasted no time telling me about the real fear that had first motivated her to call my office. The strange sounds and poltergeists in her apartment, she explained, could be dismissed perhaps as the result of natural causes. But the other phenomena taking place were more terrifying because they were having physical effects upon her body. One morning, she continued, she went into the kitchen to fix breakfast when she heard the growl of a dog behind her refrigerator. Startled, thinking at first her roommate Allison had bought a dog, she looked behind the refrigerator to discover that there was no dog anywhere to be seen. As she went ahead preparing breakfast, thinking that the noise had been her imagination, she again heard the low growl of a dog—the sound the animal makes when it is stalking prey. Then, suddenly, there was a burst of scratching sound on the kitchen linoleum floor, as if an animal with large nails or claws was darting across the floor. It was a very distinctive tapping sound that was definitely something running through her apartment. She has now heard it several times, and on a few occasions has found what appears to be dog hairs around the refrigerator.

Two nights ago, Chieko continued, she had a strange dream in which she was chasing a rabbit through a wooded forest. The rabbit was fleeing from her as it leaped over fallen trees and burrowed through the brush. She was running at a level which was at eye level with the rabbit, as if she were on all fours. One thought compelled her—to eat the rabbit, which she finally caught in her mouth. The animal screeched horribly as Chieko used her teeth to rip off the head, devouring the body and tearing off the tiny legs. Licking up the warm blood, she then felt an urge to move on through the forest for more prey. When she came to a small clearing, she saw the back of a naked woman sitting on a log. Overwhelmed with a hungry lust for blood, she leaped at her human prey just as the terrified woman turned around. It was as she tore into the woman's throat when she realized that she was her own victim! The human being that she was killing was Chieko Park! At that moment, she woke up in a cold sweat, her sheets soaking wet from her perspiration.

Then she became aware of a stinging sensation on her rear right hip. She looked in the mirror and was horrified to see that there were dog scratches on her hip, deep enough to draw blood. When she looked full view in the mirror she realized that these scratches were actually all over her back! Her back was streaked in tiny red scratches as if an animal had been in bed with her, ripping her flesh during the night! It was finally at that point when she called me for advice concerning her problem at the Pearl Vista Condominiums.

As she brusquely finished her story, the lunches arrived. Somehow I had lost my appetite for the pieces of ginger chicken that were all chopped up on my plate as if left there by a serial killer. She was waiting for my reaction as I took a quick swallow of ice water. I wanted to tell her that "I don't do dog spirits," due to a little altercation that had taken place over 10 years before, but I didn't even want to say that much. I wanted out of Chieko Park's problem as fast as possible.

"I'm not an exorcist or anything like that," I said forcefully, all my plans for a paranormal investigation thrown out the window. "I guess you called the wrong person. Sorry. How's your beef stew? This place also has a great grilled pork chop with chicken wings. You gotta try it sometime." I was not very subtle in my attempt to change the subject.

"I'm sorry to hear you say that. You once helped me. . .well, I should say you helped my parents once. They were always grateful to you."

I looked at Chieko with a puzzled frown. I always hated forgetting names or faces, so I tried to seem positive in my answer, like "oh yeah, I remember." But I couldn't, until she finally took her sunglasses off.

"Surprise! Remember? It's me, Dawn!"

I nearly fell over backwards in my chair staring into the smiling face which 12 years ago sent me to St. Francis Hospital and an extended retreat to Moloka'i to try to heal terrible facial wounds left by an *inu-gami,* a dog spirit. The last time I had seen this face it was the color of yellow jaundice and emaciated, transforming itself into a vicious beast that tried to rip open my throat. The years had added healthy flesh to her face, but now I remembered why those scars on the tips of her fingers had caught my eye. The last time I saw Dawn, she had ripped the nails out of her fingers, her bloodied hands curling like the paws of a dog. After that night I had pledged to whatever was holy that I would never again mess with canine ghosts, and here I was sitting at my favorite cafe with the very woman who had tried to kill me. By the way she acted, she almost seemed to think that I would actually be happy to see her. Was she out of her mind?

Not trying to be rude, but definitely uncomfortable sitting at the same table with Dawn, I poked at my rice with a pair of chopsticks, trying to come up with a good excuse to leave. She continued to chat away as if this were "old home week."

"My parents were very, very grateful to you Glen. They understood why you never came back to our house, or ever answered their letters. You had been hurt. I never got to say I was sorry, but I can never remember what happened."

"Neither can I really," I boldfaced lied. "Let's just drop it. Anyway, I have to. . ."

"They have both now passed away. Mom was first. Then Dad. They both died of cancer. I went on to the University of Oregon after my illness. I was there. . ."

She went on like that for 30 minutes, not even touching her food.

Filling me in on all the details of her life as if I cared, which I didn't.

"And I got married to a local Korean boy named Park. But we didn't get along. How do you like my name, Chieko? I changed it after the illness at the suggestion of a Shinto priest who said I should start a new life with a new Japanese name. I had it legally changed, so now I. . ."

Who cared about her name or her life or her wonderful new job or her divorce or anything else? I had reshaped my two scoops of rice to resemble two big dog ears, as I now realized we had hit the obligatory 50-minute time limit I impose on any luncheon or conversation during working hours.

"Well, it was nice seeing you again, Dawn. . .I mean, Chieko. A real delight. I hope that you can find someone to help you out."

I stood up abruptly, even though neither of us had finished our lunches, and walked over to the register to pay the check. Sylvia asked me if something had been wrong with the ginger chicken. She noticed that I had hardly taken one bite.

"No, it's just that I have a canine problem."

"Your teeth hurt?"

"Something like that."

I put a couple of dollars on the table for a tip, shook Chieko's hand with a half-hearted grasp and began to walk out the front door, leaving behind, I hoped for the last time, the one true force of Evil which I had in my lifetime ever faced. Chieko was stunned and a bit hurt by my obvious rejection of her and her problem, but self-interest has to take over at some point.

"Glen, I'm sorry if I did something bad to you. I never knew I did it, really. I have no memory of that night. But my parents are gone. I'm alone. Please, you are the only one I can turn to about this. I don't want it to happen again. Don't abandon me."

"I'm sorry. I can't."

Her sobs were the last thing I heard as I went through the door, turned and hurried down a sun-drenched Mo'ili'ili sidewalk as dark memories swirled shapeless in my haunted mind.

Saturday, January 6, 1996—1:00 AM

I can't sleep. Thoughts of 1984 keep flooding my dreams and waking moments. The past can be buried only so long, when suddenly a piece of that history is uncovered and then, uncontrollably, the floodgates of memory open. Sometimes I deeply regret having first written that article about the tale of *inu-gami* for the *Hawai'i Herald.* I never even read *Obake,* leaving my only copy on my bookshelf unopened. The thought of seeing that night of terror permanently contained in a book has always left me greatly unsettled. Had I done the right thing, allowing Dawn's demonic possession to be shared with the public? [Note: Arnold Hiura, once the editor of the *Hawai'i Herald,* a journal for Hawai'i's Japanese American community where the ghost stories in *Obake* first appeared, took on the task of compiling and editing that book. I never even allowed myself to reread the *inu-gami* chapter.]

At the time of the unhappy incident, Dawn had been a 22-year-old recent University of Hawai'i graduate who had been suffering from social withdrawal. Her family at first thought that she was having a mental health disorder following her self-imposed isolation in her bedroom after her loss of employment at a department store and her break up with her boyfriend. My friend and ghost story collector associate Raymond Funamoto and I had been invited into the case by a neighbor of Dawn's parents who had alerted us to the supernatural dimensions of the case. Raymond and I witnessed several strange occurrences at Dawn's Pu'unui home during several exorcisms that were conducted on the young, sickly woman. During another exorcism rite performed on the night of September 24, 1984, I was suddenly assaulted by the possessed woman who in my mind appeared as a vicious dog foaming at the mouth. Her assault required some stitches to my neck, chest and face, as her teeth ripped into my flesh.

Only one other time in my life had I been similarly attacked by a dog. When I was a child growing up near Culver City in Los Angeles, California, we lived next door to a dog trainer who prepared all the stunt animals for the television series *The Adventures of Rin Tin Tin.* There were several beautiful German Shepherd dogs which were the stunt doubles for the canine star of the show. It was great fun to climb up on the fence and watch Mr. Barnes pace the animals through their routines, jumping fences, leaping between platforms, or racing in a rotating cage. Having a "movie star" dog in our backyard (even if it was only the stunt double), was a great honor to brag to anyone who would bother to listen.

When I was 10 years old, all of my neighborhood friends and I were playing in a little rubber wading pool in our yard. Mr. Barnes later said that all of the laughter and shouts of the children had aroused his dogs, who wanted to join in the fun. They weren't trying to hurt any of the children. But as I was playing in the pool, the dogs suddenly jumped over the fence. All of the children ran into the house, but I was knocked down into the pool by one of the dogs. The animals wouldn't let me get to my friends, grabbing me in their teeth and dragging me around the yard, jumping on top of me and scratching the hell out of me. It was as if I was one of those "bad guys" in the TV show who were always mauled at the finale by Rin Tin Tin. After about 10 terrifying minutes, I was eventually rescued by my mother, who had to leap over a fence to chase the dogs away and carry my bleeding, scratch-covered and trembling body to safety. It was a living nightmare out of my childhood that had come to life when I first became personally involved with the incident of *inu-gami* possession.

Dawn or Chieko, or whatever the hell her name is now, doesn't understand how deeply afraid I am of dogs, both the living and spirit breed. I have a right to say "no" to her. I will not get involved again in this type of supernatural crap.

Sunday, January 7, 1996—4:00 PM

Is a dog spirit ever good? Does it always have to be evil? I have spent two full days researching these questions, finally mustering up the courage to face my fears. As a person who claims a public role as a "ghosthunter," it would be derelict to continue this irrational fear of one type of paranormal phenomena which frequently is discussed by a variety of informants. The problems which Chieko faces in her apartment may not even at all be related to *inu-gami.* There may have been a dog who lived in there before she moved in who died in the apartment. I have heard many stories about dogs who die and then revisit the site of their former lives. Pet owners have many stories about seeing the spirits of their beloved dogs or cats.

Hawaiian beliefs concerning dogs certainly shows that are animals with a special connection to the spirit realm. A dog howling in the night indicates the impending death of someone in the family. When Pele's little white dog is seen it is sometimes interpreted as a harbinger that a loved one has passed away. It is also believed that a dog can see the spirit of someone who has recently left their body. Tales also abound in the Islands about *'ilio,* dogs who guard certain valleys or ponds. For example, some legends of Nu'uanu talk about a dog named Poki who protects the entrance to the valley at Kapena pond. This miraculous, black-haired dog can assume any size it wishes, growing as large as a horse or stretching its neck like a giraffe.

In Chinese lore, dogs could take human shape, sometimes appearing as the dead to deceive the living. Dog-demons were abusers of women and the white dog was especially feared as a portent of death. There were dogs with human faces in China, as well as blue dogs and tailless black dogs called *p'eng-heu,* which were evil spirits. Yet, these same animals could be used to ward off evil. The faces of dogs were placed at the four gates of a palace to keep the thieves away and thus guard the house. White dogs were sometimes killed and the gates of a house smeared with their blood to ward off disaster. The barking of dogs was also believed to keep evil bird spirits away from Chinese babies.

Although in Japan the dog was sometimes beheaded so that an *inu-gami-moichi* or "dog spirit witch" could control the spirit of the mutilated beast, the dog could also be a protective spirit in Japanese lore. There are many stories about dogs who help human beings. In an eleventh century tale, a woman who earned her living by raising silk was distraught when one by one her silkworms died. When only one silk-producing worm survived, her little white dog ate it. Miraculously, from each of the dog's nostrils, strands of silk appeared. The woman pulled on these strands, which seemed to have no end. When she had piled up a great wealth of snow-white silk, her dog died. She buried him under the mulberry tree, believing that the animal was a Shinto god who had helped her in her distress. In a thirteenth century story, an ailing priest is nearing death when he has a vision of a big white dog laying near his pillow. He reaches out and snatches a handful of hair from the dog, which then vanishes. The priest's health is immediately recovered and the dog's hair is still preserved in the treasury of Hodo-in, a Buddhist temple in Kyoto.

In Asian and Polynesian belief, I have reassured myself, the notion of Evil and Good are not played out in cosmic proportions as found in Judeo-Christian belief. Demons may be evil in Asia, but, like human beings, they can also be reasoned with and utilized for positive, protective reasons. Interestingly, the word "demon" is of Greek origin from the word DAIMON, meaning "replete with wisdom." To the Greeks, daimon were guardian angels. Although the *inu-gami* spirit may invade the body of the possessed, turning the human into a raging, rabid beast foaming at the mouth and attempting to commit all kinds of foul and sometimes sexually gross and violent behavior, the spirit can be fed, spoken to and driven out of the victim. Even the *inu-gami* can be reasonable. We are not dealing with the Devil Incarnate.

My initial rejection of Chieko and her problem, I have decided, is therefore merely a hysterical reaction to her possession 12 years ago, mixed with my own childhood fears of a dog attack. There is no justification for me to believe that the dog in her apartment can't be safely sent away for the protection of this woman who looks to me for assistance. Ultimately, I have decided to make peace with my own demons. Tomorrow I will telephone Chieko.

Monday, January 8, 1996—5 PM

A very positive day. Before I had a chance to call Chieko, she called me to apologize for surprising me. She admits that she should have told me from the first moment on the telephone last week that she was "Dawn." Since she had read the Obake book, she assumed that I had gotten over the events of 1984 and would actually be happy to see her doing so well with her life, even if she was now having these new problems. She was at first frightened by the presence of a dog spirit in her apartment, but she is very reassured that now I will be her "good luck charm."

I laughed and told her that she'd need more than a good luck charm. We needed an *ikibotoke,* a living saint, to get rid of her *inu-gami* once and for all. I also mentioned to her that it was unfortunate that Senator Spark Matsunaga had passed away before he was able to write about his father who had been a powerful *ikibotoke* on the island of Kaua'i, performing many exorcisms on victims of animal possession. I had once met the Senator in Washington, D.C., and discussed my desire to record his many tales of witnessing *inu-gami* possession. He informed me that he was intending to write a book about these miraculous events, so he politely declined sharing too much information with me. Unfortunately, it seemed as if his death curtailed the book of recollections which would have been a stunning contribution not only to the history of Japanese in Hawai'i, but to the power of Island supernatural traditions.

Chieko then told me that she had a friend who went to a temple in Aiea that did mystic healing. Maybe one of their spiritual healers could come to the apartment and purify the rooms. I encouraged her to pursue that avenue while I called Raymond Funamoto to explore what ideas he had. As a devotee of ghost stories and Japanese religious practices, perhaps he had heard about some new cult that could release the force of the *inu-gami* from Pearl Vista. I feel surprisingly upbeat as old ghosts are laid to rest.

Monday, January 8, 1996—9:00 PM

Strange phone call with Raymond Funamoto. This genial, good-natured man seems a bit disturbed that I have called him. We have not communicated with each other much since 1984, but I never felt there was any "bad blood" between us. He is very curt on the telephone as I try to catch up on the latest news in his life. Finally, exasperated, he blurts out.

"This is about Dawn, right?"

"Oh," I said, a bit surprised at his mentioning of her name. We never, ever talked about this event when I had finally returned from my convalescence on Moloka'i. "Did she call you already?"

"No," he answered sharply. "I just know. I don't want anything to do with it."

"Do with what?" If she hadn't called him, how had he known about "it."

"You know exactly what I mean. You're a fool if you get involved."

The phone slammed down in my ear as if Raymond was furious. I had expected some hesitation on his part, but, after all, he wasn't the one sent to the hospital. And he was the big fan of ghost story author M.R. James. I was the one who was supposed to be terrified, not him.

A few moments later the phone rang. It was Raymond Funamoto.

"I'm sorry, Glen, for being so abrupt," he said in his usual kind voice. "It is only that my priest warned me not to even talk about this with anyone."

"It was many years ago, Raymond," I tried to reassure him. "I'm certain it is all right to talk about it now."

"Many years ago?" he said a bit satirically. "It was just the other night. I saw *inu-gami* in my dream. It was chasing a rabbit which it caught and ripped apart. Then I saw it stalk a young, naked girl sitting on a log. When the inu-gami jumped on her, I saw that it was Dawn. I woke up in a cold sweat. I talked to my priest and he told me that the demon has come back. He told me to expect your call. On his advice, I will not talk further with you about this evil. But you must listen to me. Get out of it now. Before it is too late."

He didn't wait for my "good-bye" or "thank you" for the warning, but again hung up the receiver.

Hmm. Just when I thought I was making personal progress.

Wednesday, January 10, 1996—12:00 PM

Chieko called. I didn't tell her about Raymond Funamoto's warning, but I'm acting more cautious about becoming personally involved in the haunting of Chieko's apartment. She must have sensed my hesitation, for she repeatedly asked me if something was wrong. I assured her I was just fine. The blessing is set with a Reverend Seiko Abe, one of the ministers at the Aiea church, who will be at the Pearl Vista condo on Friday evening at 6:00 PM. I agree to attend.

Friday, January 12, 1996—10:00 PM

This evening I attended the blessing of Chieko's Pearl Vista condo. In attendance at the ceremony was Rev. Abe, Chieko, Chieko's roommate

Allison, Allison's nephew, and myself. Standing only five feet tall, smartly dressed in a crisply ironed long-sleeve white blouse and simple blue pleated skirt, Rev. Abe was not the mystic I had imagined dressed in flamboyant robes and draped in amulets. She looked almost like a young school girl with her short-cropped hairstyle and her freshly white tennis shoes and knee-high white stockings. Although she must have been 40 years old, considering the extensive training required for a minister in this popular Japanese sect, she didn't look one day over 20 years. A former resident of Tokyo, she had lived in Hawai'i for about five years, becoming one of the leading teachers of this popular healing religion.

She asked, for privacy sake, that nothing that happens during the ceremony ever be revealed to anyone outside of the room, certainly not in any future book. I agreed to keep the ritual a private affair, but, with her permission, could say that it involved meditative prayer conducted in a hypnotic "hum" which as the time passed seemed to weaken my sense of balance. It was literally as if my head began to spin lightly and, although we were all supposed to kneel, I nearly collapsed to the floor, unable to maintain the ritual pose.

Nothing particularly strange or supernatural took place during the ceremony, although Rev. Abe did say that many spirits inhabited this building, spirits both unhappy and dangerous. Whether or not an *inu-gami* was present, she was unable to tell us. But the many bodies which had been disturbed to build the condominium had set forth a spiritual imbalance, which she wished to correct through her prayers.

The ceremony lasted about one hour, following which we all bowed to Rev. Abe, who left with a small envelope provided to her by Chieko. All of us felt very relieved that the ceremony had gone so well. Allison, who actually had not believed that the apartment was haunted and who knew nothing about "Dawn's" earlier demonic possession, looked a bit unconvinced by Rev. Abe's "exorcism." Allison worked for one of a local television's news department as an associate editor and, although she was born and raised in Hawai'i, had very little interest in the Islands' supernatural beliefs. A single woman in her mid-twenties, the only thing she feared was being saddled with her sister's son for an evening of baby-sitting. It put a crimp in her usual Friday night steam-blowing at Restaurant Row near downtown Honolulu.

Her five-year-old nephew actually was a very well-behaved boy who became quickly bored during the ceremony and went off into the bedroom to play with one of his fancy toy cars. He was, in fact, playing with his toy when Allison called after him following Rev. Abe's departure. He didn't answer. Concerned, she looked into the bedroom.

"Hey, you guys," she suddenly said with a laugh, "come look at my nephew. Maybe he is becoming a priest!"

Curious, Chieko and I joined Allison at the door to her bedroom to see what was so funny. On the floor, her little nephew was sitting with his legs crossed, his eyes wide-open, looking into deep space, and his arms lifeless at his side. The child was absolutely trance-like. We had no idea how long he had been sitting like this while all of us had been in the other room participating in the blessing.

Allison took her nephew by the shoulders and gave him a quick shake. He continued to look enraptured, when finally he made a little noise. It may have been my overactive imagination, but I swore that it was like a deep growl was softly emanating in the back of his throat. Then he spoke, as chills went through all of our flesh.

"I'm Demon. Call me Demon. You're a good-looking bitch, Dawn."

The childish voice was oddly deep and dirty, coming from the mouth of an innocent, sweet-looking Japanese boy. Allison later told us that this child was so well-behaved, so gentle and pure-of-heart, that it was unbelievable that he could have playacted something so foul. Chieko ran from the room in a burst of tears, as the little boy simply shut his eyes, laid down on the floor and curled up in a deep sleep. We put him back to bed, pulled the covers over him and turned out the light.

Chieko was nearly hysterical with fear in the living room, having heard the little child make lewd sexual remarks to her in the peculiar deep voice of a being named Demon. I urged her to call Rev. Abe back immediately; for the child's safety, a blessing should be conducted as soon as possible. I made my apologies to both of them for then suddenly rushing off, but I had decided Raymond was right. All of us, including Chieko, have to nip this off in the bud. I told her to move out of the building. Just get out. I would be the first. I tried not to slam the door on my way out.

Thursday, February 8, 1996—3:30 PM

It has been several weeks since the incident at Chieko's Pearl Vista condo and I have judiciously avoided all contact with the person who I believe is the source of this deadly return of the *inu-gami*. She calls my office here and at the college at least once every day to see if she can talk to me. It has gotten to the point where I don't answer my own phone. The staff have been instructed that if we get a call from anyone named Chieko Park, take a message, thank her for the call and then throw the message away. She is not to be allowed on any public program, so they must tactfully tell her that the tour is filled. When the person who takes tour reservations finally told me that she had run out of excuses, I told her to tell Chieko I'm dead. That would get rid of her. Everyone now simply refers to her as "Ms. C."

Sometimes when I drive up to my office, day or night, I see her car parked in the lot behind our old Mo'ili'ili building. I just hit the gas pedal and keep right on driving. At the end of my downtown haunted Honolulu walking tour last night, she was waiting for me at the Punchbowl Street entrance to the old KawaiaHa'o Church graveyard. As everyone left by that entrance, I disappeared among the night shadows of the tombs through the back entrance. When I got back to my car parked in front of the Territorial Building, there was a note scrawled on an old envelope.

"Stop avoiding me. I need to talk to you. It's urgent. Please, Glen, you must hear me out."

I know I've treated her shabbily, but damn it! I'm frightened!

Friday, February 9, 1996—10:00 AM

I came the work this morning to find a note tacked up on the wall saying that "Ms. C." called and that it was urgent. I've told no one why I have a dread of this woman, so everyone must think it is a jilted lover. This woman is ruining my life so I have finally decided to have it out with her. I called her at her working place and spoke as frankly as possible, my stomach tied into knots, waiting for a big confrontation. I can't be responsible for her problems, I told her. I have my own problems; she'll just have to work this out alone. I said I appreciated that she respects me, but a priest would be better in this situation. Call Rev. Abe, I insisted.

She hardly spoke on the telephone as I was pouring out my tirade. All she said when I finished was that she doesn't care what I think. If she could she would never see me again for the rest of her life. But Rev. Abe had necessitated my presence at the final exorcism of the *inu-gami.*

"I don't appreciate being ignored," she went on to say with a real edge of anger in her voice, "when all I'm trying to do is to help both of us. My dreams have gotten worse. Whether you like it or not, she says you are involved. She knows about the Portuguese *fatsetta.*"

"What do you mean?"

"About your hair turning white."

In October of 1981 I held the first "Da Kine Chickenskin: A Ghost Story Conference" at McKinley High School. During one discussion session, a Portuguese woman with spiritual power, a healer called in that culture a *fatsetta,* announced that she had worked with a family whose child had been possessed by an *inu-gami.* I was surprised by her knowledge of the history and lore of the Japanese dog spirit which she had tried to exorcise from this child. During her presentation, she looked at me and spoke very matter-of-factly that I had an *inu-gami* right behind me!

"The dog spirit is looking at you, son. He's waiting to attack you."

Later that day a man in the audience came up to me and whispered that a most incredible thing had happened when the *fatsetta* had told me that an *inu-gami* followed me about through life. At that very moment the hair at my temples had actually turned white! I rushed to the bathroom to check, and was surprised to find that my first white hairs had appeared exactly as that audience member had described. I remember feeling for the first time in my life that I, too, would age and decay. I was 34 years old the day the illusion of my eternal youth died.

I wasn't certain how Rev. Abe knew about the *fatsetta* and my white hair, but this information wasn't a total secret. Other persons in attendance that morning, I later learned, had also seen the hair at my temples turn white. They may have talked about it to their friends and maybe Rev. Abe, many years later, heard the rumor. This didn't prove anything.

"She says our lives are intertwined, whether you want them to be or not. You be at the purification tonight. Or it will get worse."

I sensed that she was right. Our lives were intertwined. The only way to sever them was to get rid of this *inu-gami,* once and for all.

"Where should I be and at what time?"

"Ten o'clock tonight. At my parents' house in Pu'unui."

"Wait a minute. I'm not going back. . ."

Before I could protest, she hung up the phone. I assume that Rev. Abe needs to go to the site where the dog spirit had first taken over her body to finally send it back to the hell from which it came. My presence was required because I had been its physical victim. Chieko had been its spiritual victim.

I trust this is not my last journal entry. I pray there will be an epilogue.

February 23, 1996—8:00 AM

I've waited for my 49th birthday to record what I hope will be the last time I use the words *"inu-gami"* and "Glen Grant" in the same sentence. Not that I am any longer afraid of this entity, if such a creature ever existed. The supernatural explanation is the easiest, but not necessarily the most true. The beast which we have been fighting is of superhuman strength, but is not born of a satanic hell—for in the last few weeks I have learned that sometimes the demons of this world can be far more deadly than anything conjured up by the devils on the other side.

I arrived at 10:00 PM, as instructed, at the Pu‘unui home which had been the scene of our 12-year-old encounter. A large "For Sale" sign was displayed on a front lawn overrun with weeds and untrimmed ferns and brush. This house, I could see, had been deserted for several years, probably after the death of Chieko's parents. I understood that selling a house where you had grown up is very difficult, but she had allowed this place to be so abandoned that vandals had used it for their nighttime amusements. Graffiti was all over the outside walls and the windows had been boarded over with huge plywood boards in an attempt to keep out the homeless, who on occasion must have used the house for shelter.

Unfortunately, the neighbors' homes on either side were unlit, giving the abandoned home an even more melancholy and dark feeling. It was so hard to believe that 12 years ago, a local family was enjoying all the pleasures of life in this simple little cottage. I recalled a very compassionate father and loving mother tormented by a fear for their daughter's wavering sanity, greeting me at a front door that now, more than a decade later, sagged on its hinges, broken and smashed by mindless vandals. The last time I walked through that door, I was going in the opposite direction, with a police escort and ambulance sirens blaring in the still midnight of the valley. I involuntarily scratched my cheek where the scars left by the inu-gami could still be faintly seen.

It was almost cathartic walking through the dark, abandoned living room, which was littered in trash and broken bottles left by the vagrants. Spray paint across the mantle indicated that teenagers must have also broken in, "tagging" their mark of pride on the interior walls. I called out for Rev. Abe or Chieko, but there was no answer. The corners of each room, I noticed, were covered in a complex of undisturbed spider webs dotted with flies and other insects trapped in the snare over the years. A gecko let out its little croak, as a large cockroach scurried across the floor into the empty kitchen at the approach of my step.

"Is that you, Dr. Grant?" a voice called out from the darkened back rooms. "Am I blessed by your presence?"

"Chieko?"

"I'm back here. And my name is Dawn tonight." Her tone was friendly, although perhaps a bit flippant. I thought it was unusual for her to call me Dr. Grant. I didn't like the way she said "Dawn."

"Is Rev. Abe here yet?"

"No, not yet," Chieko answered from the back bedroom. "She wants us in here, though. She'll be here in a minute."

I walked down the dark hallway to the very bedroom which I remembered so well from many years before. A large black moth planted high on the wall hardly stirred as I passed by. Under my feet you could hear the crunch of broken glass.

"Chieko, is there any light in here? It's kind of dark, yeah?"

"I don't need any light, Dr. Grant. I lived my whole life in this house. I used to play hide-and-go-seek with my daddy when I was a little girl. I knew every place to hide. He used to be my best friend when I was young. He died in his bed from lung cancer right in this house. He was only 48 years old. Younger than you now, yeah?"

Her voice was coming from the empty bedroom, but in the darkness I couldn't see exactly where she was. A window was open, but outside a darkened night sky made it impossible to see. My eyes couldn't adjust.

"So, when do you expect Rev. Abe? Maybe I should wait outside on the porch?"

"My mother died three years ago. I couldn't sell the house, but I didn't want to live here. My husband moved everything out for me. She died when she was 52 years old of breast cancer. Young, yeah? They both died young. How old are you, Dr. Grant?"

"I think I better go, Chieko. I'll wait outside. Why don't you join me?"

"My name is Dawn, Dr. Grant."

Finally a cloud moved a bit in the sky and a tiny ray of moonlight came into the window so that I could see the outline of Chieko sitting in a dark corner of the room. It is unbelievable, I thought to myself, how fast a house can deteriorate when it is abandoned. The cobwebs were thick in the window frame and glittered white when the moonlight struck them. A fetid smell of cockroach and rat droppings filled the closed air.

"Listen, I'm sorry if I've been rude to you. It is nothing personal. It was just that I've been frightened by all this. And it doesn't help staying in here. Can't we go outside?"

I heard a tiny tearing sound now in the room, like someone ripping up sheets of paper. I would have left with or without Chieko, but when she talked about her parents I felt remorseful for how I had acted. They were very kind people and would not have appreciated my abandonment of their daughter.

"You've been frightened? I thought you were the brave ghost man. You became famous because of me, yeah? I know you did. You made *Obake* about me and became famous. And when I ask you to help me, you can't even return my calls?"

The tearing sound became louder as the cloud now passed completely from in front of the moon. A full stream of illumination came fully through the window, bathing Chieko in a spotlight, like an actress upon a stage during her soliloquy. She was sitting stark naked on the floor, her legs crossed with a book in her lap. Next to her was a bottle of cheap wine which she had been heavily imbibing. There was no telling how long she had sat there on the filthy floor in the dark, getting drunk. Something long and pointed was in her right hand which she was using to slice the pages of the book with slow-motion gestures, cutting through the book with a deliberate, deadly ease. It was a copy of *Obake.*

"I made you famous," she kept repeating slowly, slicing now through the cover. "Now the bastard has no time for me."

She was sobbing deeply as she plunged her knife one page after another through the book which had first described the horror of the *inu-gami.* What kind of hellish mistake had I made turning this girl's pain into public entertainment? I tried to tell her how sorry I was, but I, too, was now choked with tears. I had never meant to hurt anyone, I can remember telling her. I felt that I, too, had been a victim. Could she forgive me?

I felt strangely drawn to her as I leaned down to take the shredded book out of her hand, to console her and convince her that whatever she wanted me to do, I'd be pleased to help.

"When Rev. Abe arrives, we'll make peace with the past," I told her. "All right?"

I had my hand on the book, kneeling down in front of her as she gazed downwards to the mutilated story which had forever captured her pain. Her eyes then looked up at me, slightly drunken, reddened from her weeping and tinged with mad rage.

"Rev. Abe isn't coming. I made that up. It was the only way to get you here."

A burning sensation struck my left shoulder blade as her knife sliced into my back, leaving a deep puncture wound that began to bleed profusely. I was so stunned I flew backwards to the floor as her body leaped at me, the blade of the knife again attempting to pierce my flesh. Her face I saw briefly was twisted with hatred as I grabbed her arm, twisted it sharply and made her drop the weapon. I towered over her as I stood, the blood now streaming through my shirt and hot on my back. I was planning to back out of the room when a huge wine bottle struck my cheek right below my right eye. An incredible fire of pain erupted as I backhanded her away from me. She continued to lunge forward with her bare fists, the nails that had grown back now used to once again open up my flesh.

It wasn't self-defense that now overwhelmed me, but a desire that I now understand must occasionally enter an enraged mind—a desire to murder. I am even now embarrassed to admit to the fact that within me this curse of Cain was dormant, waiting to be unleashed. That beast in my heart now howled like a banshee as I let forth a stream of garbage about Chieko and what I was going to do to her. I grabbed her throat in my two hands that felt suddenly Herculean as I threw her down to the floor, my body pouncing upon her and my curled fist plunging again and again into her defenseless features now bloody and bruised. She looked up at me with horror at what I had become as my eyes burned wildly and my teeth, feeling especially sharp and deadly, poised themselves above her. A growl came from my throat as I eyed a pulsating vein in her neck, an artery that swelled so nicely I could smell the blood inside. I hungered to open up her neck with my teeth as my jaw tightened, set to kill my frightened prey.

At that moment, someone leaped over a fence that time had removed many years before and snatched a child from the teeth of the beasts. It sounds ridiculous, but somewhere in my mind I heard a voice speak to me, helping me to lift above the scene of what I was about to do. I instantly returned to my body, thanking my mother's spirit for saving me and that poor girl from our own dementia. I immediately released Chieko, getting up off her bruised body.

I turned and walked out of the room as Chieko, sobbing uncontrollably, tried to hurriedly put on her clothes. My back was throbbing and my cheek was inflamed where she had struck me with the bottle. I couldn't say I was sorry for having tried to murder her; I was too dumbfound by my own behavior. I had frightened myself more than any ghost had ever done. I left her behind in the house of her youth, as I prayed for both our poor, violent souls.

My physical wounds healed quickly, but I've been tortured by the beast I found within. At Raymond's suggestion, I went to his Shinto priest, who tried to explain to me through an interpreter that the *inu-gami* had been in me for many years, even before the same kind of beast had attacked Chieko in 1984. When my self-control weakened that night, it finally could take over. Both Chieko's life and mine, the priest concluded, were linked through divine karma as victims of these demon spirits. He performed one more blessing over me, he explained, to help guard me from the inu-gami which at every moment hovers near me.

I don't know how I got this spirit. Was it one of the dogs who had tried to attack me as a child? Was it from a former incarnation when possibly I had been an inu-gami-moichi, a dog spirit possessor in feudal Japan? Or was it simply my inheritance of being human, capable of violence and rage which too often in this world is turned to abuse others? I knew a simple blessing would never be enough to contain this dark beast. All the priests in the world couldn't have exorcised that inu-gami within me. It was left to one loving, mothering spirit to snatch me from Hell, the spirit which on this day nearly half a century ago brought me from her womb to this bewildering mystery of existence.

Postscript—February 25, 1996.

Today I received a very nice note from Chieko. It was left at my office with a little package.

Dear Glen:

After all these years of hating me, I hope now you have found a place in your heart to forgive me. Can you now understand that the thing that made me hurt you years ago is also inside of you? I'm sorry for getting drunk. I don't know what made me want to kill you. I think telling other people about inu-gami is important. Tell the whole world what you and I both know, that inu-gami exists in you as well as me. I pray that we both will be able to control it. Good luck and please try to stay in touch with me. We have a lot in common.

P.S. A little gift for you is in the box. I'm trying to keep a healthy sense of humor about all of this.

Chieko Park

I opened the box to find a gourmet milkbone with a pretty bow tied around it. I giggled and felt just a little easier. The next time I go to Blockbuster, I told myself, I have to rent *The Adventures of Rin Tin Tin.* After all, I feel oddly related to the star.

Ku'ulei spent four days in the State mental hospital under close examination for having tried to kill her husband and son. Criminal charges were not pressed, since the physicians determined that she had shown symptoms of a mild schizophrenia which they suggested would require extensive therapy. Having your wife or daughter labeled "mentally ill" when she had for so many years conducted herself in a wholly "normal" manner was difficult for David and Ku'ulei's mother. David opted for hospitalization; the mother insisted upon a spiritual blessing to remedy the demonic possession possibly caused by Ku'ulei's occult-dabbling former friends. With great reluctance, David acquiesced to the exorcism.

Cathy described to me what took place during the ceremony at Ku'ulei's Kahalu'u home. The kahu of the mystic Hawaiian church on Kaua'i conducted the exorcism of the *noho* or possessing spirit. Ku'ulei was told to lie down on the floor with her feet towards the front door while the kahu performed a *kuehu* or shaking out the spirits utilizing a *ti* leaf. From head to toe, Ku'ulei's body was struck lightly with the ti leaf. When her entire body had been tapped, the kahu then went to the front door, where she vigorously shook the ti leaf, as if she were shaking out a dust cloth. As she did so, she said loudly, "'Ho'i no 'ai I kou kahu," "Go back and destroy your keeper." In this way the spirit had been taken out of Ku'ulei's body, dispelled from the house and returned to the person who had been responsible for the possession. The *ti* leaf would later be placed under Ku'ulei's mattress in the bed where she slept. Then the entire family, under the guidance of the kahu, performed a *ho'oponopono* ritual of setting right all of the family problems.

The psychiatrists were very hesitant to allow Ku'ulei to return to her everyday life without regular counseling because she had demonstrated definite streaks of homicidal violence in her mental outbreak. However, the immediate family was absolutely convinced that the demon who had made Ku'ulei ill had been expelled from her life. To celebrate her return to good health, the relatives decided to have a huge *lu'au* in Ku'ulei's honor. Turkeys and a fat pig were put into the *imu,* huge tents with long tables and folding chairs were put up in the backyard of the Kahalu'u home to accommodate nearly 200 guests and a well-known Hawaiian band, cousins of Ku'ulei, was invited to perform. Knowing that I had been kept privately informed of all of the secret events surrounding Ku'ulei's possession, Cathy invited me to join her at the party. Most guests of course knew that Ku'ulei had been brought back to O'ahu with an illness, but they didn't know about the attack upon her family, the diagnosis of the doctors or the exorcism.

By 1:00 AM, most of the guests had left, with only a "hard-core" group of beer drinkers singing in the backyard. I had drifted into the kitchen with Cathy, talking story with a small group of the immediate family that sat about a large table. One by one, everyone started to either leave or move into the living room, where they found a place to sleep on the floor or couch. It was about 2:00 AM when I realized that the only people still sitting at the kitchen table were Ku'ulei and me. She was still glowing from all the attention she had gotten that evening. About her neck was a beautiful *lei* of fragrant *maile* leaf intertwined with a strand of sweet-smelling *pikake*. Her conversation was very animated and upbeat, discussing with me the possibilities of going back to school to complete her master's degree. Having only met her for the first time that evening, I understood why Cathy and she were best friends. I couldn't connect the image of Ku'ulei who had sunk into mental illness on Kaua'i with this delightful person in Kahalu'u.

"Do you think I've been away from school too long," she asked me sincerely, "to be able to get back into study?"

At that point, Ku'ulei's eyes both started twitching uncontrollably, the eyelids fluttering like little wings of an insect attempting to take flight. It is difficult for me, nearly 20 years later, to describe the next anatomical change in her face without feeling a chill down my back. The dark brown pupils of both eyes suddenly turned up into her head, leaving only clear white eyeballs looking at me from across the table.

What manly voice spoke to me from the soul of Ku'ulei I cannot say, but it identified himself as Kuwahailo, the "Ku-maggot-mouthed." He knew that I was a *haole,* and he told me, in the filthiest language I have ever heard, what he thought about *haole* and what he was going to do to me. He described how he would rip out my heart and destroy me and every one of my kind. The expletives were out of the gutter when he told me what he does to Ku'ulei sexually when they are alone, and what he will do to Cathy, who is his next victim. The words which I could never repeat in any publication because of its filth and racial abhorrence, didn't come from Ku'ulei. I knew they were flowing from the bowels of some dank, putrid region of human existence guided to the surface by a being which was the nemesis of *pono,* true goodness.

The episode lasted for less than a minute or so, then Ku'ulei's pupils dropped back down into their normal position. The voice within her changed back to the kind woman with whom I had been having a most pleasant conversation. I was so stunned by the brief encounter with the satanic force that I literally was in a state of silent shock.

"So, what do you think?" Ku'ulei continued in her train of thought, unaffected or unaware of what had just taken place. "Do you think I can pick up my study habits? I want to do well in graduate school."

"I think you'll do just fine," I said emotionlessly, not wanting to even mention what just happened in case it would bring the demon back. "Gosh, it is getting so late. I better get going. It is a long drive back to town."

"You can sleep here," she politely suggested. "We got plenty of space on the floor!"

"No," I answered getting up, "I better get on home. Tell Cathy I'll call her tomorrow. Nice meeting you."

On the long, lonely and very dark ride over the Pali Highway that night, I kept hearing in my head the voice of Kuwahailo, wondering what impostor this was from within Ku'ulei. Was it simply a mental illness which this young woman would need to face if she ever had hope of leading a rewarding and rich life? Or was it something else very real, with a separate existence from this one poor victim, something which one day in my life, if I continued walking my ghost-strewn pathway, I would need to confront?

That week I found a letter on the subject of demonic possession written by William James, the great American philosopher and contributing founder of the American Psychic Research Society, in the 1890s. A distinguished Harvard philosopher of pragmatism and cultural pluralism, James investigated paranormal medium trances in an attempt to understand the psychic powers which may link us subliminally in a spiritual universe. "I shall not ignore," James wrote to a fellow investigator of supernatural phenomena, "the sporadic cases of old fashioned malignant possession which still occur today. I am convinced that we stand with all these things at the threshold of a long inquiry, of which the end appears as yet to no one, least of all to myself."

The long inquiry continues, as we still ponder the boundary line between sanity and spirit. In subsequent years, Ku'ulei's problem seemed to have gone away. I don't know if she ever spoke to anyone again as she had done to me that night, but her marriage on Kaua'i, with two more children, has been secure for over two decades. Cathy was never possessed by Ku'ulei's demon or for that matter the devils of anyone else. I did tell her what had happened between her cousin and myself that evening, so she had herself properly blessed. That Christmas she even sent me a little present, a beautifully hand-carved bone turtle which was her *'aumakua* or family spirit. She had one made for herself and one for me. She wasn't certain whether an amulet of her guardian angels would protect me, but there was no harm in trying.

Today that precious protector sits on my desk, hopefully warding off all those filthy things dark and sinister that wait, and wait, and wait for a vulnerable moment.

CITY OF HONOLULU
VICE
SQUAD
TERRITORY OF HAWAII

The Casebook Sealed

Four touchstones to the world beyond. An old, battered Honolulu Police Department "Vice Squad" badge taken from the corpse of a murdered cop in a shallow grave. "A Spiritual Letter" written in backwards, automatic writing with a planchette owned by one of America's most beloved poets. An old, faded photograph of an *obake* house, a photograph that killed the person who snapped it and imparted to its current owner the power to kill just through the focus of hate. A hand-carved, turtle amulet of an *'aumakua* who protects the soul of the living from the demonic invasion of foul spirits.

Four touchstones to the otherworld forming a puzzle of cosmic proportions.

What awaits us on the day of our death?

What lurks in the shadows of the land beyond the grave?

Is it benevolent and blessed? Or evil and cursed?

Two days after my father's funeral in December 1973, I had intended to return to Honolulu on a morning flight out of Los Angeles. The night before my departure, I stayed up with my mother until 11:00 PM., both of us somewhat exhausted by the grieving. We were the only ones in the house that night as we said "goodnight" and went off to our beds. I slept in the back room, which many years before my father had built himself as an addition to the only house which I have ever known as "home."

I cannot say that I woke up that night to the presence of my father standing next to me. In my heart I have tried to convince myself many times that I was not dreaming, that I had indeed opened my eyes. Yet, somehow, it doesn't matter if I were in a dream or a waking state of mind. I only know and believe that it was the spirit of my father standing next to me. His body seemed to radiate a wonderful glow.

Instead of rushing home the day I had heard he had gone into the hospital with a relapse of his cancer, I asked my mother if it would be all right to wait until my classes at the University of Hawai'i were over. No one anticipated his death so unexpectedly, so they said that my delay would be a good idea. We didn't want to frighten father with the family all hurrying to his bedside as if he were immediately dying. Unfortunately, my father passed away just a few days before my last class. I never got to tell him how much I loved him and how grateful I would forever be for his giving me my very first ghost story. I never told him "aloha."

This guilt poured forth as he stood next to me as I lay in my bed that night. Perhaps my guilt had brought him back. I tried to say that I was sorry for not being at his side when he died, but then I realized, he was not dead!

"You're not dead! Dad, you're not dead!"

He smiled at me and answered with his usual sense of humor that I had loved him for in life.

"Of course I'm dead, you stupid kid. I'm dead. But, Glen, I am still alive."

I started to laugh that he didn't make sense. All I knew was that my father had not passed away. He was in the room with me and I could tell him everything that I had failed to do when he was still in the flesh. But, before I could say a word, he spoke again.

"There are things on this side you must never know. What you are doing now is all right, but don't go further. Collect the stories, but be cautious. Remember, I'll always be there with you."

With those words, he bent over and for the only time in my life that I could remember, my father, who in life seemed sometimes very cold and remote, kissed me. His radiating light bathed me in a white aura as I felt the peace of his lips upon my forehead. I drifted off to sleep, only to be awakened later by my mother screaming in my ear that I had missed my airplane. Both of us that morning had slept so peacefully that we had not heard two alarms going off. My flight to Hawai'i was at 9:00 AM and it was already 10:00 AM when both of us finally awoke.

Perhaps it is wishful thinking, but since that night I have always believed that my "guardian angel" watches me as I share and explore the supernatural of Hawai'i. I am protected, as I pray you are, from the dark side of the cabinet. For that reason, I try not to be *niele* or nosy about things that don't concern me, because I remember always his warning. Sometimes when

I lead a group of people into Honolulu's downtown graveyard, I smell the scent of my father's familiar, pungent witch hazel hair lotion waft pass me. The smell, I know, must come from a plant or tree on the graveyard grounds, but it doesn't matter. I feel secure and protected—for I know, as I reseal The Secret Obake Casebook, the spirit who gave me my first ghost story will protect me from whatever dark forces exist in this world or the next, until I finally tell the last ghost story.

Glossary

adobo (Filipino), chicken or pork simmered in vinegar, garlic, and soy sauce.

akua (Hawaiian), ancient gods.

akua noho (Hawaiian), god possession.

aloha (Hawaiian), love, affection, compassion, a greeting or salutation.

Amityville horror, a sensational supernatural case in the 1970s which captured national attention concerning a terrifying haunted house in Long Island, N.Y. about which a film and book were written. The haunting later was reported to be a hoax.

'apo leo (Hawaiian), a form of magic where a sorcerer catches the voice of the victim and uses it to kill him.

aswang (Filipino), a vampire, ghost or witch that can take many threatening forms.

automatic writing, writing done in a dissociated or altered state of consciousness that is attributed to spirits of the dead.

'aumakua (Hawaiian), family or personal gods, deified ancestors.

banshee, a female death omen spirit of Ireland and Scotland that attaches itself to families and frequently makes a wailing sound at the impending death of a family member.

bull liar (pidgin English), someone who tells tall tales.

chicken skin (pidgin English) a tingling sensation in the skin caused by an emotional response of fear, awe, or wonder. An island term for "goosebumps."

cockroached (pidgin English), to steal.

demi-god, a mythological being with more power than a being, but less than a god.

'e'epa (Hawaiian), miraculous creatures.

evil eye, a widespread folk belief that certain individuals can harm and kill with a glance.

fatsetta (Portuguese), a person with spiritual power, a healer.

futon (Japanese), bedding or mattress.

haole (Hawaiian), foreigner, specifically a Caucasian.

hara kiri (Japanese), ritualistic suicide.

hoʻailona (Hawaiian), an omen or portent.

holua (Hawaiian), a sled used on grassy slopes.

hoʻomana (Hawaiian), to worship, religion.

hoʻopiʻopiʻo (Hawaiian), a type of magic where the practitioner touched a part of his own body which in turn inflicted pain at the very same place on the victim's body.

hoʻoponopono (Hawaiian), a ritual used in the family to set things right.

hoʻounauna (Hawaiian), a form of sorcery where a message of death was sent directly into the body of the victim.

hula halau (Hawaiian), a school of Hawaiian dance.

ʻieʻie (Hawaiian), an endemic woody, branchy climber which grows in the upland regions of Hawaiʻi.

ikibotoke (Japanese), a living saint used to perform exorcism and other benedictions.

ʻilio (Hawaiian), a dog.

ʻili ʻouli (Hawaiian), a variety of "skin signs" which are used to sense a spiritual presence.

imu (Hawaiian), an underground oven.

incubus, a female spirit supposed to work evil on men in their sleep.

inu-gami (Japanese), a dog spirit used in magic.

inu-gami-moichi (Japanese), a witch who uses the dog spirit.

kahu (Hawaiian), honored attendant, guardian or keeper.

kahuna (Hawaiian), priest.

kahuna ʻanaʻana poʻokoʻi (Hawaiian), "adz-headed kahuna" who were beheaded for practicing sorcery.

kahuna kilokilo (Hawaiian), a priest who specializes in studying the stars for the purposes of divining omens.

kahuna kuni (Hawaiian), a priest who through ritual could heal people being prayed to death, sending the curse back to the source.

ka lawe maunu (Hawaiian), a ritual used in sorcery which involves burning the clothing of the intended victim.

kama'aina (Hawaiian), a native-born resident of Hawai'i.

kane o ka po (Hawaiian), a male spirit or dream lover, literally the "man of the night."

karaoke (Japanese), a Japanese invented form of "singalong" entertainment popular in Hawai'i.

kasha (Japanese), an invisible, cannibalistic folk creature that tears human beings asunder.

ka'upu (Hawaiian), a Laysan albatross which breeds on the northwestern Hawaiian Islands

ke 'oni (Hawaiian), a magical rite where the sorcerer writhes like an eel which causes his victim to fall down in pain imitating the motion.

kichigai (Japanese), madness, insanity.

kilokilo 'uhane (Hawaiian), a magic ritual to call back the spirit of the dead.

kotonk (pidgin English) a term used by island Japanese Americans to refer to Japanese Americans raised on the mainland U.S.

kuehu (Hawaiian), a ritual of shaking out the spirits.

kumu (Hawaiian), a goatfish.

kupua o ka po (Hawaiian), a wizard of the night,

kupuna (Hawaiian), grandparent, ancestor, relative or close friend of the grandparent's generation.

lau hala (Hawaiian), pandanus leaf, especially as used in plaiting.

lei (Hawaiian), a garland or wreath.

lua (Hawaiian), pit.

lu'au (Hawaiian), Hawaiian feast.

lumpia (Filipino), a deep-fried crepe filled with vegetable and meat filling.

McKinley Tigers, the well-known name for the sports teams at McKinley High School in Honolulu.

mahalo (Hawaiian), thanks, gratitude.

maile (Hawaiian), a native twinning shrub.

makaloa (Hawaiian), a perennial sedge found in or near fresh or salt water used to make mats.

make (Hawaiian), to die or perish.

malihini (Hawaiian), newcomer, stranger or visitor.

mama and papa-san store (pidgin English), a neighborhood mom-and-pop store.

mana (Hawaiian), supernatural or divine power.

maunu (Hawaiian), bait used to perform rituals of sorcery.

Menehune (Hawaiian), a legendary race of small people who worked at night building fishponds, roads, temples.

Merrie Monarch Hula Festival, an annual hula competition featuring hula halau from around the world held in Hilo, Hawai'i, in honor of King Kalakaua known affectionately as the "Merrie Monarch."

mimi (Hawaiian), urine.

Morgan's Corner, a well-known O'ahu place on Nu'uanu Pali Drive and the Old Pali Road which is alleged to be haunted.

mu'umu'u (Hawaiian), a loose gown.

necromancy, the magical art of raising the dead from their graves.

niele (Hawaiian), to keep asking questions, curious, nosy.

nightmarchers, a night procession of Hawaiian spirits who march on certain days of the month, on certain paths.

noho (Hawaiian), a possessing spirit.

noho ia (Hawaiian), a wild spirit possession.

obake (Japanese), a supernatural being, monster or ghost.

odaisan (Japanese), a folk priest who contacts spirits of the dead to protect or heal the living.

'ohana (Hawaiian), an extended family.

'okakala (Hawaiian), a sensation of goose flesh indicating the presence of a supernatural being.

'okole (Hawaiian), the buttocks.

'okolehao (Hawaiian), liquor distilled from ti root in a still of the same name.

Ouija board, a game which is popularly used to contact spirits of the dead.

oyako donburi (Japanese), a bowl of rice topped with chicken and a slightly cooked egg.

pakalolo (Hawaiian), marijuana.

paniolo (Hawaiian), cowboy.

pau hana (Hawaiian), to finish work.

p'eng-heu (Chinese), tailless black dogs which were considered evil spirits.

pi kai (Hawaiian), ceremonial sprinkling of salt water.

pikake (Hawaiian), the Arabian jasmine named after the peacock since the Princess Kai'ulani was fond of both the flower and the bird.

pilau (Hawaiian), somewhat bad-smelling.

pilikia (Hawaiian), trouble of any kind.

planchette, a device used to receive written messages from the spirits of the dead, it is a platform on three legs, two of the legs being attached to wheels and the third to a pencil.

pokpoklo (Filipino), sea vegetable.

poltergeist, a noisy, mischievous ghost held to be responsible for unexplained noises.

pono (Hawaiian), true goodness.

pu hala (Hawaiian), the pandanus tree.

pule 'ana'ana (Hawaiian), praying to death through sorcery.

pule kuni (Hawaiian), a prayer used to reverse a prayer of death.

pu'olo (Hawaiian), a bundle or package.

pupule (Hawaiian), insane.

saimin (pidgin), a local expression for hot noodle soup.

sashimi (Japanese), slices of raw fish.

seance, a spiritualistic meeting to receive communication from the spirits of the dead.

sensei (Japanese), teacher.

shaka (pidgin English), a hand gesture with extended thumb and pinkie finger to signify a variety of meanings including hello, okay, or "I got it!"

synchronicity, a belief that all "coincidences" have a meaningful relationship.

succubus, a male spirit supposed to work evil on women in their sleep.

swipes, a home-brewed alcoholic drink made from fermented pineapple, potatoes or other fruits or vegetables.

Sympathetic magic, the belief that the future can be manipulated through the use of physical objects or body parts from the person to be injured.

Theosophy, a religion founded by Helene Blavatsky which claimed to have contact with Tibetan adepts who communicated through Mme. Blavatsky through automatic writing.

ti leaf (Hawaiian), a woody plant in the lily family. Green ti leaves are believed to afford protection from spirits.

trance medium, a person who is capable of "channeling" messages from the spirit world.

tsunami (Japanese), a tidal wave.

'uku (Hawaiian), flea

'ukulele (Hawaiian), the musical instrument brought to Hawai'i from Portugal. Literally means "leaping flea," probably from the nickname of Edward Purvis, who was small and quick and who popularized the instrument in the Islands.

voodoo, an African-West Indies religion based upon African ancestral worship that employs sympathetic magic, fetish rituals and trance.

wahi i ka Paipala (Hawaiian), the act of opening the Bible and selecting a passage at random as a means to seek help in a problem.

wahine o ka po (Hawaiian), a female spirit or dream lover, literally "woman of the night."

witchboard, a Ouija board

witch's tit, a mark upon the body which was identified in the sixteenth and seventeenth centuries as the place that the Devil or his demons kissed and sucked witches.

zabuton (Japanese), a cushion.

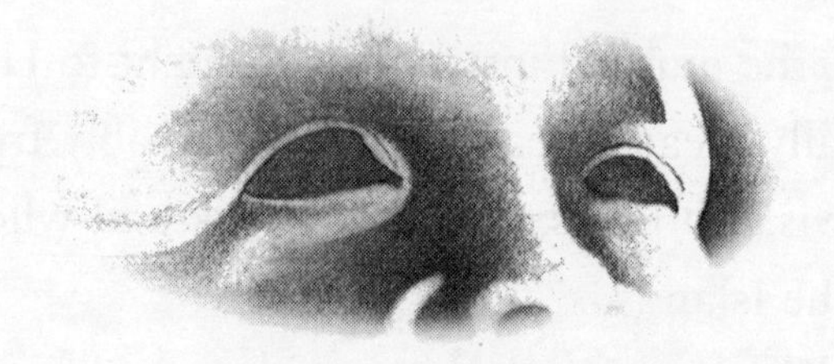

The book is completed,
And closed, like the day;
And the hand that has written it
Lays it away.

Dim grow its fancies;
Forgotten they lie;
Like coals in the ashes,
They darken and die.

Song sinks into silence,
The story is told,
The windows are darkened,
The hearth-stone is cold.

Darker and darker
The black shadows fall;
Sleep and oblivion
Reign over all.

Curfew
Henry Wadsworth Longfellow

Glen Grant has been collecting and telling the supernatural tales of Hawai'i for over twenty-five years as a teacher, cultural specialist, storyteller and author. His 1981 "Da Kine Chickenskin" conference, followed by conferences in 1982, 1985 and 1991, helped to first promote and perpetuate the supernatural heritage of the Islands as a legitimate, fascinating field of study. Dr. Grant received a doctorate in American Studies from the University of Hawai'i completing his dissertation on the popular supernatural beliefs of nineteenth century American culture. He has spoken to audiences of all ages and backgrounds throughout the Hawaiian islands, entertaining tens of thousands of islanders at public and private schools, community organizations, hotels, and businesses with tales of the supernatural as well as the history of Hawai'i. In 1986 he launched the "Ghosts of Old Honolulu" haunted walking tour in downtown Honolulu which has grown to be one of the most unique cultural tourism programs in the islands offering over fifteen different monthly historical and ghostlore excursions. He was awarded the Tusitala Award by the Storytelling Association of Hawai'i and was honored as a "Living Treasure of Multiculturalism" by the City and County of Honolulu.

His tales of mysteries have all been island best-sellers, including Obake: Ghost Stories of Hawai'i, Honolulu Mysteries: Case Studies in the Life of a Honolulu Detective and Obake Files: Ghostly Encounters in Supernatural Hawai'i. He is the host of Chick'n Skin: Supernatural Tales of Hawai'i annual television series and Chicken Skin: The Radio Show, a weekly "talk story" show on KCCN 1420 AM radio. An instructor of American Studies at Hawai'i Tokai International College, Dr. Grant resides in Mo'ili'ili, what he boasts as the most haunted neighborhood in Honolulu.